# Recent Results in Cancer Research 56

Fortschritte der Krebsforschung
Progrès dans les recherches sur le cancer

# Lymphocytes, Macrophages, and Cancer

Edited by

G. Mathé   I. Florentin   M.-C. Simmler

With 53 Figures

Springer-Verlag
Berlin  Heidelberg  New York 1976

EORTC-Symposium. Held in Paris on June 26/27, 1975

Georges Mathé
Irène Florentin
Marie-Christine Simmler

Institut de Cancérologie et d'Immunogénétique (INSERM),
Hôpital Paul-Brousse, 14—16 Av. Paul-Vaillant-Couturier
94800 Villejuif/France

*Sponsored by the Swiss League against Cancer*

ISBN 3-540-07902-5   Springer-Verlag Berlin·Heidelberg·New York
ISBN 0-387-07902-5   Springer-Verlag New York·Heidelberg·Berlin

Library of Congress Cataloging in Publication Data. Main entry under title:
Lymphocytes, macrophages, and cancer. (Recent results in cancer research ; 56)
1. Cancer--Immunological aspects. 2. Immunocompetent cells. 3. Lymphocytes.
4. Macrophages. I. Mathé, Georges, 1922- II. Florentin, Irène,
1940- III. Simmler, M. -C., 1947- IV. Series.
[DNLM: 1. Lymphocytes. 2. Macrophages. 3. Neoplasms--Immunology.
Wl RE106P v. 56 / QZ200 L986]
RC261.R35 vol.56 [RC267] 616.9'94'008s [616.9'94'079]
76-26538

Typesetting, printing and binding:
Konrad Triltsch, Graphischer Betrieb, 87 Würzburg, Germany

# Contents

# List of Contributors

ALLISON, A. C., Medical Research Council, Clinical Research Centre, Watford Road, Harrow HA1 3UJ, Middlesex, England.

BALKWILL, F. R., ICRF Department of Medical Oncology, St. Bartholomew's Hospital, London EC1, England.

BELPOMME, D., Institut de Cancérologie et d'Immunogénétique (INSERM), Hôpital Paul-Brousse, 14—16 Avenue Paul-Vaillant-Couturier, 94800 Villejuif, France.

BORANIĆ, M., Laboratory for Experimental Therapy, Department of Experimental Biology and Medicine, "Ruder Boško-vić" Institute, 41001 Zagreb, P. O. Box 1016, Yugoslavia.

BROUET, J. C., Institut de Recherches sur les Maladies du Sang, Hôpital Saint-Louis, 75010 Paris, France.

BRULEY-ROSSET, M., Institut de Cancérologie et d'Immuno-génétique (INSERM), Hôpital Paul-Brousse, 14—16 Avenue Paul-Vaillant-Couturier, 94800 Villejuif, France.

CAILLOU, B., Institut Gustave Roussy, 16 bis Avenue Paul-Vaillant-Couturier, 94800 Villejuif, France.

CATOVSKY, D., M.R.C. Leukaemia Unit, Royal Postgraduate Medical School, London W12 OHS, England.

DANTCHEV, D., Institut de Cancérologie et d'Immunogénétique (INSERM), Hôpital Paul-Brousse, 14—16 Avenue Paul-Vaillant-Couturier, 94800 Villejuif, France.

DAVIES, A. J. S., Department of Radiotherapy, Royal Marsden Hospital, Sutton, Surrey and Department of Immunobiology, Chester Beatty Research Institute, Institute of Cancer Research, London, England.

DAVIGNY, M., Institut de Cancérologie et d'Immunogénétique (INSERM), Hôpital Paul-Brousse, 14—16 Avenue Paul-Vaillant-Couturier, 94800 Villejuif, France.

FEUILHADE DE CHAUVIN, F., Institut de Cancérologie et d'Im-munogénétique (INSERM), Hôpital Paul-Brousse, 14—16 Avenue Paul-Vaillant-Couturier, 94800 Villejuif, France.

FLORENTIN, I., Institut de Cancérologie et d'Immunogénétique (INSERM), Hôpital Paul-Brousse, 14—16, Avenue Paul-Vaillant-Couturier, 94800 Villejuif, France.

GABRILOVAC, J., Laboratory for Experimental Therapy, Department of Experimental Biology and Medicine, "Ruder Boškovié" Institute, 41001 Zagreb, P. O. Box 1016, Yugoslavia.

GAUCI, C. L., Dept. Experimental and Clinical Immunology, Centre Paul Lamarque, Hôpital St. Eloi, 34059 Montpellier, France.

GOMARD, E., Laboratoire d'Immunologie des Tumeurs, Hôpital Cochin, 75014 Paris, France.

GRANDJON, D., Institut de Cancérologie et d'Immunogénétique (INSERM), Hôpital Paul-Brousse, 14—16 Avenue Paul-Vaillant-Couturier, 94800 Villejuif, France.

GREGORIADIS, G., Medical Research Council, Clinical Research Centre, Watford Road, Harrow HA1 3UJ, Middlesex, England.

HRŠAK, I., Laboratory for Experimental Therapy, Department of Experimental Biology and Medicine, "Ruder Boškovié" Institute, 41001 Zagreb, P. O. Box 1016, Yugoslavia.

HUCHET, R., Institut de Cancérologie et d'Immunogénétique (INSERM), 14—16 Avenue Paul-Vaillant-Couturier, Hôpital Paul-Brousse, 94800 Villejuif, France.

JOSEPH, R. R., Temple University Health Sciences Center, Philadelphia, PA 19140/USA.

KAY, M. M. B., Laboratory of Cellular and Comparative Physiology, Gerontology Research Center, National Institute on Aging, NIH, PHS, U. S. Department of Health, Education and Welfare, Bethesda, and the Baltimore City Hospitals, Baltimore, MD 21224/USA.

LAFLEUR, N., Institut de Cancérologie et d'Immunogénétique (INSERM), Hôpital Paul-Brousse, 14—16 Avenue Paul-Vaillant-Couturier, 94800 Villejuif, France.

LECLERC, J. C., Laboratoire d'Immunologie des Tumeurs, Hôpital Cochin, 75014 Paris, France.

LELARGE, N., Institut de Cancérologie et d'Immunogénétique (INSERM), Hôpital Paul-Brousse, 14—16 Avenue Paul-Vaillant-Couturier, 94800 Villejuif, France.

LEVY, J. P., Laboratoire d'Immunologie des Tumeurs, Hôpital Cochin, 75014 Paris, France.

LHERITIER, J., Institut de Cancérologie et d'Immunogénétique (INSERM), Hôpital Paul-Brousse, 14—16 Avenue Paul-Vaillant-Couturier, 94800 Villejuif, France.

MATHÉ, G., Institut de Cancérologie et d'Immunogénétique (INSERM), Hôpital Paul-Brousse, 14—16 Avenue Paul-Vaillant-Couturier, 94800 Villejuif, France.

MAUEL, J., W.H.O. Immunology Research and Training Centre, Institut de Biochimie, 21, rue du Bugnon, 1011 Lausanne, Switzerland.

OLIVER, R. T. D., ICRF Department of Medical Oncology, St. Bartholomew's Hospital, London EC1, England.

PINON, F., Institut de Cancérologie et d'Immunogénétique (INSERM), Hôpital Paul-Brousse, 14—16 Avenue Paul-Vaillant-Couturier, 94800 Villejuif, France.

POLJAK-BLAŽI, M., Laboratory for Experimental Therapy, Department of Experimental Biology and Medicine, "Ruder Bošković" Institute, 41001 Zagreb, P. O. Box 1016, Yugoslavia.

PREUD'HOMME, J. L., Institut de Recherches sur les Maladies du Sang, Hôpital Saint-Louis, 75010 Paris, France.

RADAČIĆ, M., Laboratory for Experimental Therapy, Department of Experimental Biology and Medicine, "Ruder Bošković" Institute, 41001 Zagreb, P. O. Box 1016, Yugoslavia.

SELIGMANN, M., Institut de Recherches sur les Maladies du Sang, Hôpital Saint-Louis, 75010 Paris, France.

SENIK, A., Laboratoire d'Immunologie des Tumeurs, Hôpital Cochin, 75014 Paris, France.

STATHOPOULOS, G., Department of Radiotherapy, Royal Marsden Hospital, Sutton, Surrey and Department of Immunobiology, Chester Beatty Research Institute, Institute of Cancer Research, London, England.

WILKINSON, P. C., Department of Bacteriology and Immunology, Western Infirmary, University of Glasgow, Glasgow G11 6NT, Scotland.

# Chapter 1
# Morphological Recognition of Lymphocytes and Macrophages

D. CATOVSKY

The identification of lymphocytes and monocytes and their subpopulations is important in the diagnosis and classification of leukaemias
and lymphomas. Both cell types undergo morphological changes related
to their function, which may lead to confusion particularly in histological sections. The frequent use of the non-specific term "mononuclear
cell" indicates the difficulty in identification.

## LYMPHOCYTES

Lymphocytes of similar origin may appear morphologically different,
depending on whether they are in a resting stage or have undergone
blast transformation following mitogenic stimulation (11). On the other
hand, lymphocytes belonging to different populations (e.g. B or T) may
appear morphologically indistinguishable by light or transmission electron microscopy (EM). The concept of differentiation and maturation
as ordinarily applied to cell development is not helpful in the case
of lymphocytes which are better characterized in terms of their surface
markers (13)

The above points are well-illustrated in the various lymphoproliferative
disorders. Monoclonal B-cell proliferations may have a wide spectrum
of morphological appearances, yet they share identical profiles of
membrane markers. Morphologically "well-differentiated" lymphocytes in
chronic lymphocytic leukaemia (CLL) may have a similar pattern of surface-bound immunoglobulins to seemingly "poorly differentiated" cells
in Burkitt-type acute leukaemia (8) or to the intermediate cells in
prolymphocytic leukaemia (PLL) (9). On the other hand, it seems that
in terms of immunological development the CLL lymphocyte is "less differentiated" than Burkitt's tumour cell (13). Similarly, T-cell proliferations may range morphologically from undifferentiated blast cells
in T-lymphocytic leukaemia (3), which usually lack the deep basophilic
cytoplasm seen in Burkitt's cells, to cells which may morphologically
resemble lymphocytes, as seen in some patients with Sezary's syndrome
(16).

Cytochemical tests have been used in a attempt to improve the recognition of the various lymphocyte populations. A perinuclear ring of PAS-
positive granules has often been associated in our experience with
chronic B-cell leukaemias (CLL and PLL) (4). In the acute leukaemias
the PAS reaction does not show consistent results, but strong acid
phosphatase positivity, almost exclusively localized to the lysosomal
granules and membranes of the Golgi region, have been shown to correlate
with T-cell leukaemias both at light (2, 4) and EM levels (3). This
characteristic pattern of reaction has also been observed in a small

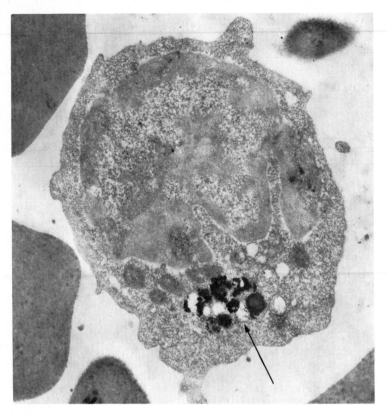

*Fig. 1. Normal T-lymphocyte forming rosette with sheep red cells showing a strong acid phosphatase reaction in the Golgi region (arrow) (x23,000)*

proportion of normal T-lymphocytes forming rosettes with sheep red cells (Fig. 1) and in a relatively higher proportion of PHA-transformed T-lymphocytes (Fig. 2); in the latter the reaction is associated with increased endocytosis by the stimulated cells (1).

The use of membrane markers is valuable for characterising populations of lymphocytes as B or T cells. It may also prove helpful in distinguishing lymphocytes from monocytes. Some of the techniques for surface markers can be applied in combination with morphological observations; correlations can then be made between cell morphology and immunologically defined receptors. Surface immunoglobulins can be demonstrated in B-lymphocytes at EM level by means of antisera conjugated with horse-radish peroxidase (12); this new technique has, in turn, made possible a more accurate description of the villous surface of the B-lymphocyte. T-lymphocytes and lymphoblasts which form spontaneous rosettes with sheep red cells can be visualized morphologically in cytocentrifuge preparations (Fig. 3) CLL B-lymphocytes and cells from "hairy" cell leukaemia have been found to form spontaneous rosettes with mouse red cells (6). Other rosetting systems, e.g. for the demonstration of Fc and $C_3$ receptors, can be applied not only to cell suspensions but also to histological sections (10). The systematic use of these techniques will increase the sensitivity of our methods for cell recognition and will, in conjunction with morphological techniques, increase the standards in classification and, consequently, in the treatment of lymphoproliferative disorders.

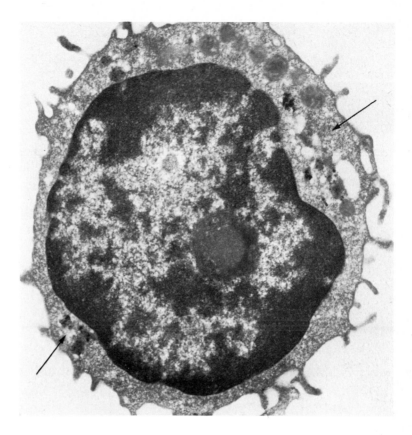

Fig. 2. *PHA-transformed T-lymphocyte showing acid phosphatase reaction in membranes of the Golgi region and in vesicles of endocytosis (arrows) (x30,000)*

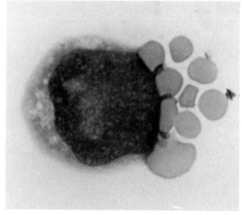

Fig. 3. *T-lymphoblast forming rosette with sheep red cells; cytocentrifuge slide; May-Grünwald-Giemsa stain (x1,500)*

The study of the cellular components of the recently defined mononuclear-phagocyte system (MPS) (15): promonocytes, monocytes and macrophages (histiocytes), presents similar problems to that of the lymphoid system. The stages of cell differentiation are not always easily identifiable morphologically; macrophages can acquire the capacity for cell division, and thus take on some features which suggest de-differentiation.

Cytochemical tests useful for the study of monocytes and their precursors have been well-documented (14). A strong positivity with the non-specific esterase reactions (using naphthol-AS acetate or α-naphthyl acetate as substrates) which is sensitive to NaF inhibition is one of the characteristic features. Cytochemical tests for myeloperoxidase at EM level are useful for recognizing early monocyte precursors in the bone marrow, particularly the promonocyte; the small myeloperoxidase-containing granules disappear at later stages and are usually absent in macrophages.

Cells with varying degrees of monocytic differentiation may be seen in acute monocytic leukaemia and can be clearly defined by EM, e.g from very undifferentiated monoblasts (Fig. 4), through a cell still showing an immature monocytoid nucleus but with a well-developed Golgi apparatus and some electron-dense granules (Fig. 5), to a more mature cell, with all the characteristics of a blood monocyte (Fig. 6). Blood and bone-marrow cells in cases of histiocytic lymphoma in a leukaemic stage have features in common with those seen in monocytic leukaemia. Our observations on six such cases showed that the circulating histiocytes were nearly always strongly positive with the naphtol-AS acetate esterase (NaF-sensitive) and the acid phosphatase (tartrate-sensitive) cytochemical reactions and by means of a cytobacterial method (5) they were shown to contain lysozyme to a varying degree (5-90% of the cells).

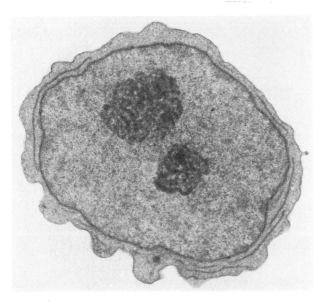

*Fig. 4-6. Electron microscopy of blood cells from a case of acute monocytic leukaemia; uranyl acetate, lead citrate staining; Fig. 4 Poorly differentiated monoblast with long profiles of endoplasmic reticulum (x15,000)*

4

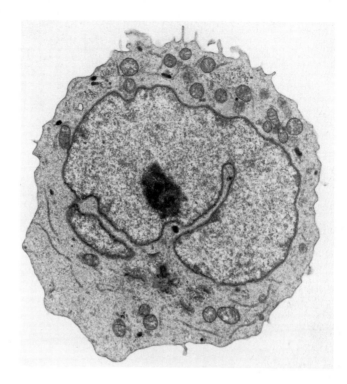

Fig. 5. More differentiated cell with an active Golgi apparatus and a few electron-dense cytoplasmic granules (x10,000)

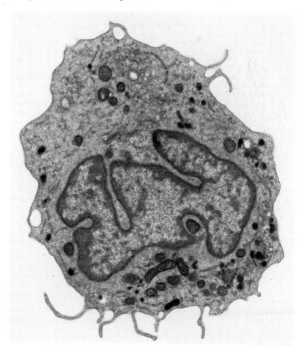

Fig. 6. Well-developed mature monocyte (x12,000)

5

Tests of monocyte function such as phagocytosis and the demonstration
of specific surface receptors can be combined with morphological techniques and thus be of great value for the recognition of cells belonging
to the MPS. Monocytes attach easily to glass surfaces and gradually
develop macrophage features in short-term cultures; these changes can
be followed in coverslips incorporated into Leighton tubes. Rosette
formation and phagocytosis by monocytes are more easily demonstrated
in such a system than by leaving the cells in suspension as for lymphocytes. Human red cells (Rh+) coated with an anti-Rh IgG antibody can
be used to demonstrate the Fc receptors of monocytes, but not of B-lymphocytes. We have demonstrated the presence of Fc and C3 receptors at
a very early stage of monocytic differentiation in several otherwise
undifferentiated monoblast leukaemias.

The application of these techniques to the study of malignancies of the
MPS will help to clarify some of the confusion still existing in the
classification of malignant lymphomas, particularly with reference to
the diagnosis of "histiocytic" lymphomas. A classification of the disorders of the MPS based on the patterns of cell differentiation has
already been suggested (7).

## Acknowledgments

The author wishes to thank Mrs. Barbara Ward for her expert technical
assistance.

## REFERENCES

1. Biberfeld, P.: Endocytosis and lysosome formation in blood lymphocytes transformed by PHA. J. Ultrastruct. Res. 37, 41 (1971)
2. Catovsky, D.: T-cell origin of acid-phosphatase-positive lymphoblasts. Lancet ii, 327 (1975)
3. Catovsky, D., Frisch, B., Van Noorden, S.: B, T and "null" cell
   leukaemias. Electron cytochemistry and surface morphology. Blood
   Cells 1, 115-124 (1975)
4. Catovsky, D., Galetto, J., Okos, A., Miliani, E., Galton, D.A.G.:
   Cytochemical profile of B and T leukaemic lymphocytes with special
   reference to acute lymphoblastic leukaemia. J. Clin. Path. 27,
   767-771 (1974)
5. Catovsky, D., Galton, D.A.G.: Lysozyme activity and nitrobluetetra-
   zolium reduction in leukaemic cells. J. Clin. Path. 26, 60-69 (1973)
6. Catovsky, D., Papamichail, M., Okos, A., Miliani, E., Holborow, E.J.:
   Formation of mouse red cell rosettes by "hairy" cells. Biomed. 23,
   81-84 (1975)
7. Cline, M.J., Golde, D.W.: Review and re-evaluation of histiocytic
   disorders. Amer. J. Med. 55, 49-60 (1973)
8. Flandrin, G., Brouet, J.C., Daniel, M.T., Preud'homme, J.L.: Acute
   leukemia with Burkitt's tumor cells: a study of six cases with
   special reference to lymphocyte surface markers. Blood 45, 183
   (1975)
9. Galton, D.A.G., Goldman, J.M., Wiltshaw, E., Catovsky, D., Henry,
   K., Goldenberg, G.J.: Prolymphocytic leukaemia. Brit. J. Haemat.
   27, 7-23 (1974)
10. Jaffe, E.S., Shevach, E.M., Frank, M.M., Berard, C.W., Green, I.:
    Nodular lymphoma-evidence for origin from follicular B-lymphocytes.
    New Engl. J. Med. 290, 813-819 (1974)
11. Ling, N.R., Kay, J.E.: Lymphocyte stimulation. Amsterdam: Nord-
    Holland, 1975

12. Reyes, F., Lejonc, J.L., Gourdin, M.F., Mannoni, P., Dreyfus, B.:
    The surface morphology of human B lymphocytes as revealed by immuno-
    electron microscopy. J. exp. Med. 141, 392-410 (1975)
13. Salmon, S.E., Seligmann, M.: B-cell neoplasia in man. Lancet ii,
    1230-1234 (1974)
14. Schmalzl, F., Braunsteiner, H.: The cytochemistry of monocytes and
    macrophages. Sem. Haemat. III, 2, 93-131 (1970)
15. Van Furth, R., Cohn, Z.A., Hirsch, J.G., Humphrey, J.H., Spector,
    W.G., Langevoort, H.L.: The mononuclear phagocyte system: a new
    classification of macrophages, monocytes and their precusor cells.
    Bull. W.H.O. 46, 845-852 (1972)
16. Zucker-Franklin, D.: Properties of the Sezary lymphoid cell. An
    ultrastructural analysis. Mayo Clinic Proc. 49, 567 (1974)

Chapter 2
# Revised Semiology of the Different Mononuclear Cells Under Scanning Electron Microscopy

D. DANTCHEV

ABSTRACT

Scanning electron microscopy shows that the thymus cell surface is not smooth but slightly undulated; this type of surface characteristic is found on the cells of several types of T-lymphocyte tumors such as T-cell lymphosarcoma, mycosis fungoides, and T-immunoblastic lymphosarcoma.

The cell surface of Frabricius' bursa is covered with numerous short villi. They are found on the cells of several kinds of B-lymphocyte tumors, including B-cell chronic lymphoid leukemia, B-prolymphocytic lymphosarcoma, and B-immunoblastic lymphosarcoma.

Mycosis fungoides cells frequently have a characteristic shape. Normal and myeloma plasma cells are similar in shape but their surface is covered with numerous characteristic tiny balls.

Immunoblasts are twice the size of so-called small lymphocytes.

In the blood and in the lymphocyte population transformed by mitogens, cell surfaces vary from completely smooth (with no undulations as in thymic cells) to villous, with short to very long villi. These variations are visible even when a constant technique and the critical-point drying method are used. Their significance, however, is not known.

INTRODUCTION

Scanning electron microscopy (SEM) is the most recent technique to be used for the examination of blood-cell morphology. BESSIS was the first to describe the different aspects of erythrocytes during the years 1970-1972. His publications contain extremely clear images of erythrocytes in various types of anemia, as well as photographs of the different stages of phagocytosis (4-9). However SEM was considered to be chiefly of morphological interest until 1973, when POLLIACK et al. claimed that the technique could be used to distinguish T- and B-lymphocytes, the former having a smooth membrane surface and the latter, a villous one (13, 15). This generated great enthusiasm for the method but critical reactions followed, based on the existence of several intermediate cell types ranging from smooth to villous, on the discovery of T cells with villous surfaces, and on the important changes in cell surfaces due to differences in methods of preparing material for examination (10, 11, 1). These changes were caused by air drying and did not occur in critical-point or freeze drying (14).

8

Using the SEM technique and, in every case, the critical-point drying method, we examined normal and pathological mononuclear cells previously identified with immune markers.

We listed the different aspects of normal and pathological lymphoid and macrophagic cells in the blood, and in the hematopoietic and lymphoid organs.

This paper aims to summarize the results of our inventory of the different aspects of these mononuclear cells.

## MATERIAL AND METHODS

Lymphomononuclear peripheral blood cells were obtained by the Ficoll hypaque density gradient technique (2). The lymphocyte suspension was washed four times and then resuspended in isotonic saline or in Hank's salt solution. Ganglion or spleen biopsy samples were crushed before being treated by the Ficoll hypaque technique. Finally, three or four drops containing at least $2 \times 10^6$ cells were placed on Flotronic silver membrane (0.05 µm porosity) for examination by SEM. The cells were then immediately prefixed for 30 min. with 2% glutaraldehyde (pH 7.25), rinsed three times with cacodulate buffer (0.1 M, pH 7.25) and post-fixed with 1% osmium tetroxide (pH 7.25) for half an hour, after which the membranes were again rinsed twice with the same buffer. After dehydration in graded alcohols (50%, 70%, 90%, and 100%) for 5 min. the preparations were immersed in Freon 113 and quickly transferred to a colled high-pressure chamber. The Freon 113 critical point was obtained with a Polaron critical-point appliance (E 3000, London). The desiccated membranes were attached to stubs and coated with a thin layer (250 Å) of gold paladium, using a Jeol vacuum evaporator (JEE - 4B). Preparations were analized under a Jeol 100 C: ASID scanning electron microscope. Micrographs were recorded on Polaroid film (type 55 P/N) at a direct magnification ranging from x2,000 to x10,000.

We studied mononuclear cells from the following sources: (a) normal mouse thymus and chicken Fabricius bursa; (b) normal mouse and human blood; (c) mouse and human lymphoid tissues; (d) human lymphocytes transformed by PHA and PWM; (e) human lymphocytes forming spontaneous rosettes with sheep red blood cells (SRBC), a process only considered possible with T-cells; (f) human lymphocytes forming immunological EAC rosettes with SRBC, a process considered peculiar to B-lymphocytes; (g) activated macrophages; (h) cells from inflamed sites such as mouse peritoneal cells after Bacillus Calmette-Guérin (BCG) injection (1 mg i.v.); (i) different lymphoid or monocytoid leukemia cells and myeloma cells, as well as cells from various types of hematosarcoma, including immunoblastic lymphosarcoma and mycosis fungoides.

The cells of all the populations studied varied in size and time of surface. We shall describe these characteristics for the median cell in each population at x10,000.

## RESULTS AND DISCUSSION

### Cell Types Observed

The surface of all normal mouse thymus cells is not smooth, but slightly undulated. Their diameter (about 4µ) is constant (Fig. 1A).

The surface of normal chicken Fabricius bursa cells is covered with numerous very small villi. Their diameter varies from 4-5μ (Fig. 1B).

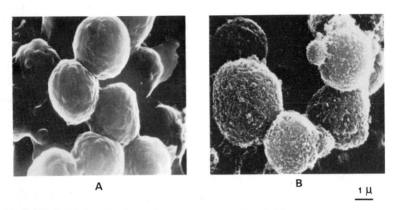

A                    B
                              1 μ

*Fig. 1. A = Normal mouse thymus cells; B = Normal chicken Fabricius cells*

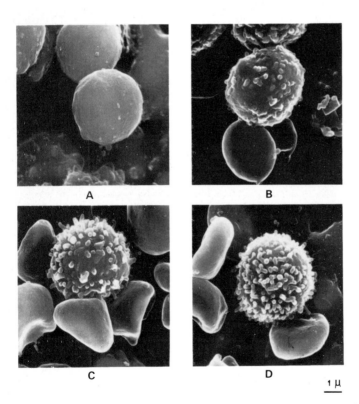

A                    B

C                    D
                    1 μ

*Fig. 2. Four most frequent types of lymphocytes in mouse, chicken, and human blood: type (A) has smooth nonundulated surface; type (D) has numerous long microvilli; type (B) and (C) are intermediate: (C) is richer in microvilli than (B) and less than (D)*

Figure 2 shows the four most frequent types of lymphocytes in mouse, chicken, and human blood: type (A) has a smooth nonundulated surface and a diameter of about 4μ; type (D) has numerous long microvilli, much longer than those of the bursa cells, with a diameter of 4.5μ; types (B) and (C) are intermediate; type (C) is richer in microvilli than type (B) on which they are less numerous than on type (D) (Fig. 2 A, B, C, D). In general, microvilli are shorter in chicken bursa than in mouse or human blood cells.

The above four blood-cell types not only differ from thymus and bursa cells, but fail to correspond to T- or B-lymphocytes, since the four types form spontaneous rosettes with SRBC (Fig. 3 A, B, C, D).

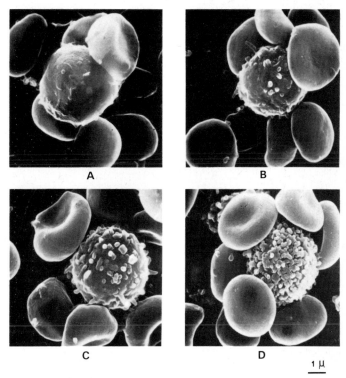

A          B

C          D

1 μ

*Fig. 3. Spontaneous rosettes with SRBC formed by 4 types of blood lymphocytes (A, B, C, D) observed in same preparation*

Lymphocytes transformed into blasts by mitogens differ from blood lymphocytes in their size, which is larger, but they may have all the surface characteristics described: smooth, undulated or villous. Microvilli may be few, numerous, short or long (Fig. 4A, B, C, D). Identical variations occur in PHA and in PWM-induced blasts, although PHA has been shown to transform mostly T-lymphocytes and PWM, both T and B cells. This observation is another argument against the exclusively smooth aspect of T-lymphocytes.

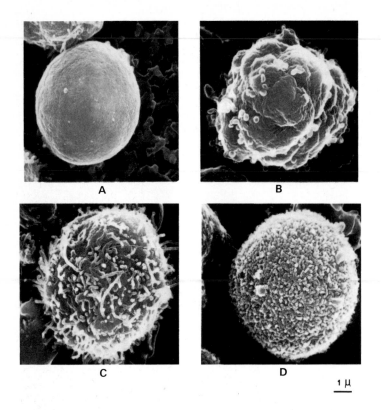

A    B

C    D

1 µ

*Fig. 4. Lymphocytes transformed into blasts by mitogens (PHA and PWM) with different surface characteristics: smooth (A), undulated (B), with long microvilli (C), and with short very numerous microvilli (D)*

However, the relatively smooth, slightly undulated surface typical of thymus cells, and the small microvilli characteristic of bursa cells are often observed on leukemia and hematosarcoma cells[a].

Figure 5A shows a typical mycosis fungoides cell, which is known to be a T cell. Figure 5B shows a T-lymphoblastic lymphosarcoma cell and (C) a T-immunoblastic lymphosarcoma cell. The first cell (A) is characteristically pear-shaped, the second (B) is round and medium-sized, and the third (C) is larger than (B). All three, however, have the same slightly undulated surface like a thymus cell.

Figure 6 shows four B-cell types: the first (A) is a B-chronic lymphoid leukemia cell, the second (B) is a B-lymphosarcoma prolymphocytic cell, the third (C) is a B-immunoblastic lymphosarcoma cell, and the fourth (D) a myeloma plasma cell. The first two cells, (A) and (B), are characterized by their small size and are both covered with small villi resembling those of bursa cells. The third (C) is similar but larger, and the fourth (D), a plasma cell, is covered with different-sized balls (from 0.5 to 2µ in diameter) and is often pear-shaped.

---

a See also the article of D. BELPOMME et al., chap. 17, for correlations between the different SEM types and the immunological findings in leukemias and hematosarcomas.

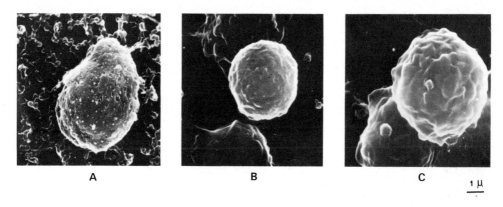

A             B             C     1 μ

*Fig. 5. A = typical mycosis fungoides cell, known to be T cell; B = T-lymphoblastic lymphosarcoma cell; C = T-immunoblastic lymphosarcoma cell*

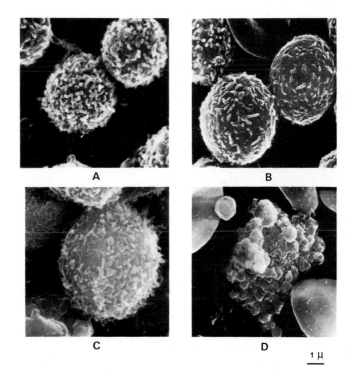

*Fig. 6. A = B-chronic lymphoid leukemia cells; B = B-lymphosarcoma prolymphocytic cells; C = B-immunoblastic lymphosarcoma cell; D = myeloma plasma cell*

Such are the aspects of the different cells in the lymphocytic series. They are easy to distinguish from blood monocytes, which have a diameter of 5-7μ, a ruffled membrane, and ridge-like profiles as shown in Figure 7A. According to the W.H.O. nomenclature (12), the histiocyte or inactive macrophage is very similar but is adherent to glass: Figure 7B shows a normal mouse peritoneal histiocyte. However, the peritoneal activated macrophages, subjected to in vivo BCG treatment, are very different and adhere completely to glass (C).

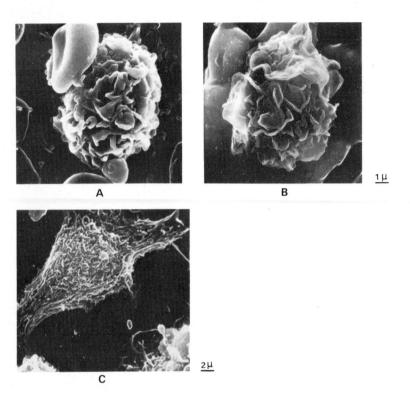

Fig. 7. A = blood monocyte; B = normal mouse peritoneal histiocyte or inactive macrophage; C = activated peritoneal macrophage subjected to in vivo BCG treatment

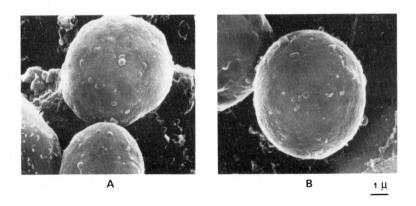

Fig. 8. A and B = reticulosarcoma cells

Finally, the cells of lymphoid organ reticulosarcoma and bone reticulo-sarcoma, both characterized by intense pericellular infiltration by very delicate reticulin fibrils, do not resemble any of the macrophages described above when examined by SEM. They are large (long diameter about 10µ, short diameter 6-8µ), their surface is smooth and they are not adherent, as shown in Figure 8 (A and B). They may be reticulum cells, as called by classical histiocytologists (4). Today, some authors consider such cells as cells of an intermediate type somewhere between hematopoietc cells and fibroblasts (17). Their smooth appearance under SEM does not support the theory that they are derived from monocytes (16). The results of SEM tend to indicate the hypothetical nature of this theory and to return the reticular cell to its traditional place in the classical reticular-endothelial system.

The classification and terminology used in this paper are those of the W.H.O. Reference Center for Leukemias and Hematosarcomas (12).

## Acknowledgements

The authors would like to thank Mrs. Ginette MARTIN for the excellent photographic reproductions of this work and Mme. Chimène BENAVENTE for the preparation of the manuscript.

## REFERENCES

1. Alexander, E.L., Wetzel, B.: Human lymphocytes: Similarity of B and T cell surface morphology. Science 188, 732 (1975)
2. Belpomme, D., Dantchev, D., Rusquec, E., Grandjon, D., Huchet, R., Pouillart, P., Schwarzenberg, L., Amiel, J.L., Mathé, G.: T and B lymphocyte markers on the neoplastic cell of 20 patients with acute and 10 patients with chronic lymphoid leukemia. Biomed. 20, 109 (1974)
3. Belpomme, D., Dantchev, D., Lelarge, N., Joseph, R., Caillou, B., Lafleur, N., Mathé, G.: Search for correlations between immuno-logical and morphological criteria used to classify lymphoid leu-kemias and non-Hodgkin's hematosarcomas, with special reference to scanning electron microscopy and T and B membrane markers. This Volume chap. 17
4. Bessis, M.: Les cellules du sang normal et pathologique. Paris: Masson, 1972
5. Bessis, M., de Boisfleury, A.: Etude sur les poïkilocytes au micro-scope à balayage, en particulier dans la thalassémie. Nouv. Rev. Fr. Hématol. 10, 515 (1970)
6. Bessis, M., de Boisfleury, A.: Etude des différentes étapes de l'érythrophagocytose par microcinématographie et microscopie élec-tronique à balayage. Nouv. Rev. Fr. Hématol. 10, 223 (1970)
7. Bessis, M., de Boisfleury, A.: Les mouvements des leucocytes étudiés au microscope électronique à balayage. Nouv. Rev. Fr. Hématol. 11, 377 (1971)
8. Bessis, M., Dobler, J., Mandon, F.: Discocytes, échinocytes dans l'anémie à cellules falciformes. Examen au microscope à balayage. Nouv. Rev. Fr. Hématol. 10, 63 (1970)
9. Bessis, M., Mandon, P.: La microsphérulation et les formes myélimi-ques des globules rouges. Etude comparée au microscope électronique à balayage et transmission. Nouv. Rev. Fr. Hématol. 12, 443 (1972)

10. Lin, P.S., Cooper, A.G., Wortis, H.H.: Scanning electron microscopy of human T-cell and B-cell rosettes. New Engl. J. Med. <u>13</u>, 548 (1973)
11. Lin, P.S., Wallach, P.H., Tsai, S.: Temperature-induced variations in the surface topology of culture lymphocytes are revealed by scanning electron microscopy. Proc. Nat. Acad. Sci. <u>70</u>, 2492 (1973)
12. Mathé, G., Rappaport, H.: Histological typing of the neoplastic disease of the haematopoietic and lymphoid tissues. Geneva: W.H.O. 1976, Vol. I
13. Polliak, A., Lampen, N., Clarkson, B.D., de Harven, E., Bentwich, Z., Siegal, F.P., Kunkel, H.G.: Identification of human B and T lymphocytes by scanning electron microscopy. J. Exp. Med. <u>138</u>, 607 (1973)
14. Polliak, A., Lampen, N., de Harven, E.: Comparison of air drying and critical point drying procedures for the study of human blood cells by scanning electron microscopy. Proceedings of the 6th Annual Scanning Electron Microscopy Symposium, I.T.I. Res. Inst., Chicago, 1973, p. 535
15. Polliak, A., Lampen, N., de Harven, E.: Scanning electron microscopy of lymphocytes of known B and T derivation. In: Scanning Electron Microscopy (Part III) 7th Annual Scanning Electron Microscopy Symposium, Chicago, 1974, pp. 673-682
16. Van Furth, R., Cohn, Z.A., Hirsch, J.G., Humprey, J.H., Spector, W.G., Langevoort, J.: The mononuclear phagocyte system: a new classification of macrophages, monocytes and their precursor cells. Bull. O.M.S. <u>46</u>, 845 (1972)
17. Wilson, F., Personal communication

# Chapter 3

# Immunologic Definition of Lymphocytes: Functions and Markers

G. STATHOPOULOS and A. J. S. DAVIES

In 1956 the lymphocyte was widely recognized as a cell of importance
in the immune response but there was little precise information. Since
that time many changes have taken place and the broad concept of a
bimodal lymphoid system has emerged. The two modalities relate both to
the immediate anatomic origin of the two cell populations in their
virgin antigenically unstimulated condition and to their functional
aptitudes. Cells from the thymus are referred to as T-lymphocytes and
those from the bone marrow (or bursal equivalent) are named B-lymphocytes. These latter, B, cells are without doubt responsible for antibody production in the classical sense but in some as yet undefined way
they are assisted in the full discharge of this function by the T-lymphocyte population. The T-lymphocyte is probably capable of cytotoxic
activity against foreign or virally infected cells in addition to its
"helper" cell function in antibody responses. There are many complexi-
ties recognized in the B- and T-cell system most of which at the present time relate to experimental animal situations from which much of
our present concept of lymphocyte heterogeneity derives.

There seems little doubt that the notion of B- and T-lymphocytes is
useful in the species Homo sapiens and we wish here to discuss the ex-
tent to which this is so. In experimental animals the recognition of
the two kinds of lymphocytes derived in the first instance from two
kinds of model experiments. CLAMAN et al. (1) first showed that trans-
ference of cells from either bone marrow or thymus into irradiated mice
which were then antigenically stimulated led to an immune response
which was smaller than when both cell populations were injected together.
This functional synergism was confirmed by the experiments of DAVIES
et al. (2) and amplified by MILLER and MITCHELL (3) who showed that it
was the B-lymphocyte population which produced antibody. This functional
differentiation lent substance to the dichotomy of anatomic origin
which had been suspected for some time. The work of RAFF (4) on the
θ-antigenicity of T-lymphocytes and the surface immunoglobulins of B-
lymphocytes in mice laid the foundations for the many methods by which
it has proved possible to "mark" and quantitate these two cell populations, firstly experimental animals and more recently in man. It is
paradoxical that we have little idea of the biological significance of
many of these marker characteristics.

Here we intend briefly to review what is known of lymphocyte markers
in mice and men and go on to show a limited series of applications of
these new methods of  description to various lymphoid neoplasias in man.

The principle marker characteristics of T- and B-lymphocytes are shown
in Table 1.

This is not intended to be a comprehensive list, which is available
elsewhere (5) but should simply serve to indicate that many marker

characteristics have been adduced and used with various degrees of reliability.

Table 1. T- and B-lymphocyte markers

| | Name | Marker for | Species of occurrence | Notes |
|---|---|---|---|---|
| Cell surface markers | θ(Thy 1) | T | Mouse | High in thymus, low in peripheral T cells |
| | Ly(Ly-A) | T | Mouse | |
| | TL | T | Mouse | Present in thymus, usually absent in periphery |
| | MBLA | B | Mouse | |
| Cell surface immunoglobulins | IgG | B | | 5% |
| | IgM | B | | The usual Ig on B-lymphocytes |
| | IgA | B | | 5% |
| | IgD | B | | High in newborn |
| Response to mitogens in vitro | PHA | T | Mouse | Can be B in special circumstances |
| | Con A | T | Mouse | |
| | PWM | T & B | Mouse & Human | |
| | Endotoxin | B | Mouse | |
| Rosetting characteristics 1. Heterologous erythrocytes (spontaneous) | SRFC | T | Human | |
| | MRFC | B | Human | |
| | (many other) | | | |
| 2. Fc receptors[a] | Fc rosettes | B | Mouse Human | |
| 3. Complement receptors[b] | EAC rosettes | B | Human Mouse | |
| EM | Hairiness | B | Mouse Human | |
| Electrophoretic mobility | | T or B | Mouse Human | |

[a] Antigen-antibody complexes of which the antigen is usually a heterologous erythrocyte.

[b] Antigen-antibody-complement complexes of which the antigen is usually a heterologous erythrocyte.

From a practical viewpoint it is clear that without massive financial
resources the description of the lymphocytes of patients with various
diseases is likely to be possible only on the basis of a selected few
of these markers.

In our own studies on human lymphoid neoplasias we have elected to use
two rosetting characteristics, one for B- and one for T-lymphocytes,
the mitogenic response to PHA in vitro as a T-cell characteristic and
the presence of immunoglobulin on the cell surface as a B-cell marker.
The techniques have been published elsewhere (6-8) and we shall not
dwell on them here except to say that it is becoming increasingly evident that lymphocytes in vitro have a very delicate physiological status and that as all our tests are based on livings cells, at least
initially, technical standardization is most important. It is worth-
while pointing out that many of the contemporary descriptions of lymphocytes depend not upon some staining artefacts of dead cells but on
artefacts of various kinds induced in living cells. In this way the
contemporary cellular immunologist has departed radically from the
older methods of haematologist and pathologist but it is still incumbent
on him to prove that the new artefacts represent a significant improvement on the informational array that the older techniques provided.
At the present time the case is not proven. Nevertheless there are clear
aims for those applying lymphocyte marker techniques. Firstly, the
immunological status of the patient may be ascertainable simply by
accurate counts of the appropriate cells. On the present evidence this
is only likely to be true for extremes of immunological hyporesponsive-
ness. In addition it should be emphasized that the standard methods
of immunoglobulin quantitation are complementary to any cell assay not
alternatives. Secondly, marker characteristics may be useful both di-
agnostically and prognostically and thirdly, the new methods may offer
much greater understanding of the natural history of the disease. This
last possibility is particularly true of the various lymphoid neoplasias.

We have chosen to present our results on various lymphoid neoplasias
organ by organ. Tables 2-7 give the results we have obtained. In Table
2 the findings from disease-free blood, bone marrow, lymph nodes and
spleens are presented. As can be seen by the SRFC and Ig+ve criteria,
T-type cells predominate in blood and lymph nodes; in spleen the percentages of B and T cells are about the same. In bone marrow the sum
of T and B percentages is not more than 50%. This is not necessarily
because there are many undefined lymphoid cells or lymphocytes, but as
can be seen from the standard May-Grünwald-Giemsa stained slides after
Ficoll-Triosil separation, many normoblasts and a few granulocytes
appear at the Ficoll-serum interface. These cells are likely to constitute most of the "null" cells in the bone-marrow preparations. Taking
into account only the lymphocytes in marrow, the T and B percentages
are approximately T - 36% and B - 64%. The PHA index seems to be positively correlated with the number of T cells determined by SRFC. The
frequency of MRFC is inadequate to account for all the Ig ve B cells
but MRFC do seem to be of particular value in the diagnosis of CLL
(Table 3). It should, however, be noted that others have described CLLs
with T-cell characteristics (9, 10). In Table 3 (CLL) B cells (% Ig+ve
cells and % MRFC) predominate in all four organs indicating that the
disease is systematized. In Table 4 the results of several cases of
acute lymphoblastic leukaemia are presented. Two of the cases given
separately had a very high percentage of T cells but in all the others
the majority of the cells were not adequately characterized by the
methods adopted. Also in one case out of two that were investigated
the B-type cells were very high in bone-marrow samples.

Table 2. Samples from disease-free specimens

| | %SRFC[a] | %Ig-ve cells[b] | Index of PHA responses[c] | %MRFC[d] | No. of case investigated |
|---|---|---|---|---|---|
| Blood | 65.8[e] 51.0-78.0 | 23.5 17.0-29.0 | 10.7 6.0-18.0 | 11.7 5.0-21.0 | 17 |
| Bone marrow | 18.0 3.0-78.0 | 32.0 11.0-76.0 | 2.0 1.0-3.9 | 4.6 1.0-8.0 | 18 |
| Lymph node | 55.8 28.0-78.0 | 25.1 6.0-58.0 | 11.6 1.1-23.6 | 9.3 3.0-28.0 | 20 |
| Spleen | 46.3 35.0-65.0 | 40.9 10.0-64.0 | 7.9 1.4-18.6 | 10.6 5.0-21.0 | 20 |

[a] SRFC: Nucleated blood cells, usually lymphocytes, forming rosettes
   when mixed with sheep red blood cells.

[b] Ig+ve cells: Surface-bound immunoglobulin-positive cells

[c] PHA index: $\dfrac{\text{count of stimulated cells} - \text{count of unstimulated cells}}{\text{count of unstimulated cells}}$

[d] MRFC: Nucleated blood cells, usually lymphocytes, forming rosettes
   when mixed with mouse red blood cells

[e] The upper figure is the mean value and the lower figure is the range

(These five footnotes also apply to Tables 3 - 7)

Table 3. Chronic lymphocytic leukaemia (CLL)

| | % SRFC | % Ig+ve cells | Index of PHA response | % MRFC | No. of cases investigated |
|---|---|---|---|---|---|
| Blood | 11.0 2.0-49.0 | 79.8 45.0-94.0 | 7.1 1.0-35.0 | 71.7 63.0-83.0 | 22 |
| Bone marrow | 9.3 3.0-17.0 | 82.3 80.0-85.0 | 5.2 2.5-7.4 | 69.3 66.0-75.0 | 4 |
| Lymph node | 18.3 14.0-22.0 | 72.0 64.0-77.0 | 14.9 5.2-28.5 | 54.5 46.0-63.0 | 3 |
| Spleen | 26.0 | 70.0 | 33.0 | 55.0 | 1 |

Table 4. Acute lymphoblastic leukaemia (ALL)

| | % SRFC | % Ig-ve cells | Index of PHA response | % MRFC | No. of cases investigated |
|---|---|---|---|---|---|
| Blood | 22.5 3.0-40.0 | 2.0 0.5-4.0 | 10.6 1.0-37.0 | 1.0-3.0 | 12 |
| Blood | 95.0 73.0 | 0.3 2.5 | 2.5 - | 1.0 7.0 | 1 1 |
| Bone marrow | 14.0 8.0 | 2.0 72.0 | 4.3 - | - 1.0 | 1 1 |

In Table 5 in one case of AMML it is shown that the great majority of monocytoblasts were Ig+ve. This table also shows that prolymphocytic leukaemias and Sternberg sarcoma cells could be either T or B in predominace. In one case of Sternberg lymphoma, cells from cerebrospinal fluid were also investigated and found to have the same characteristics as the malignant cells at other sites.

Table 5. Various lymphoid neuplasias

| | | % SRFC | % Ig+ve cells | Index of response | % MRFC | No. of cases |
|---|---|---|---|---|---|---|
| Acute myelomono- cytic leukaemia | Blood | 8.0 | 86.0 | 1.6 | 4.0 | 1 |
| Prolymphocytic leukaemia | Blood | 88.0 | -ve | 6.2 | - | 1 |
| | | 6.0 | 90.0 | 1.8 | - | 1 |
| Sternberg lym- phoma | Blood | 2.0 | 84.0 | 3.3 | - | 1 |
| | Bone marrow | 2.0 | 85.0 | 2.0 | - | |
| | Blood | 50.0 | 18.0 | 1.9 | - | |
| | Lymph node | 79.0 | 4.0 | 7.3 | - | 1 |
| | C.S.F. | 81.0 | -ve | 1.0 | - | |

In Table 6 the results from Hodgkin's patients are presented. The two organs involved by the disease were lymph nodes and spleen. A higher percentage of T cells was found in Hodgkin's lymph nodes than in disease-free lymph nodes (Table 2). The Hodgkin's spleens had lower frequencies of T cells than did normal spleen.

Table 6. Hodgkin's disease

| | % SRFC | % Ig+ve cells | Index of PHA response | % MRFC | No. of cases investigated |
|---|---|---|---|---|---|
| Blood | 50.2 27.0-77.0 | 27.9 16.0-37.0 | 8.7 1.0-16.0 | 14.5 4.0-27.0 | 20 |
| Lymph node | 66.2 44.0-88.0 | 14.4 6.0-21.0 | 8.2 1.0-24.2 | 15.5 3.0-36.0 | 10 |
| Spleen | 39.0 26.0-66.0 | 34.9 15.0-63.0 | 9.0 1.0-27.8 | 19.8 6.0-34.0 | 14 |

Finally, in Table 7 the results of non-Hodgkin's lymphomas are presented. It is important to note the findings in the lymph-node specimens. In the lymphocytic lymphomas, well or poorly differentiated, nodular or diffuse, the B-type cells were predominant. In histiocytic and reticulum cell lymphomas various results were obtained; in most cases T cells were high relative to the lymphocytic lymphomas, in other cases the proportion of undefined cells was rather high. In one case of histiocytic lymphoma B cells constituted 80% of all cells observed. In two cases of immunoblastic sarcoma T cells were apparently found. In one case of Sezary's syndrome T cells were very high. In plasmacytomas a high proportion of cells showed cytoplasmic staining and in one case of mycosis fungoides the T cells were fewer than the B cells. These last few oddities must be regarded as simply anecdotal for the moment.

The results presented do not as they stand tell us much about the immunological status of the patients involved. They do tell us that in a variety of lymphoid neoplasias there are distortions of the normal patterns of T- and B-cell characteristics. The results also show that many of these lymphoid neoplasias are widely generalized diseases which can show consistent abnormalities in T- and B-cell pattern in whatever lymphoid organ is sampled.

Table 7. Non-Hodgkin's lymphomas

| | | % SRFC | % Ig+ve cells | Index of PHA response | % MRFC | No. of cases |
|---|---|---|---|---|---|---|
| Lymphocytic lymphomas | Blood | 42.7 2.0-70-0 | 36.0 10.0-78.0 | 7.3 1.0-36.0 | low | 20 |
| Lymphocytic lymphomas | Lymph node | 21.7 3.0-40.0 | 70.9 51.0-92.0 | 7.3 1.0-16.8 | 18.1 9.0-35.0 | 13 |
| Histiocytic or reticulum cell lymphomas | Lymph node | 50.2 13.0-77.0 | 27.1 9.0-83.0 | 9.7 1.0-36.6 | 20.6 8.0-30.0 | 12 |
| Immunoblastic sarcomas | Lymph node | 70.0 49.0 | 27.0 27.0 | 5.4 1.5 | – 3.0 | 1 1 |
| Sezary's syndrome | Blood | 77.0 | 8.2 | – | 6.0 | 1 |
| Histiocytic lymphomas | Spleen | 54.0 44.0-64.0 | 39.0 – | 4.5 1.4-7.5 | 9.0 | 3 |
| Lymphocytic lymphomas | Spleen | 37.0 28.0-48.0 | 62.0 | 7.4 5.5-9.3 | 10.0 | 3 |
| Plasmacytomas | Lymph node | 12.5 0-21.0 | Cytoplasmic staining in majority of cells | 2.8 1.0-8.2 | 33.2 0.8-79.0 | 4 |
| Mycosis fungoides | Lymph node | 33.0 | 43.0 | 14.2 | 12.0 | 1 |

It appears that various diseases have a typical T- or B-cell profile, for example CLL is normally a disease of the B-lymphocyte series. It should, however, be noted that CLL cases with "T" cells have been recorded (9, 10). Lymphocytic lymphoma also seems to be a disease that usually involves B cells whereas its less lymphocytic counterpart (histiocytic or reticulum cell sarcoma) seems to have, if anything, T-cell characteristics. The diagnostic and prognostic usefulness of this kind of information may emerge in time. It also remains to be seen whether newer and perhaps more natural classifications based on lymphocyte bimodality will be widely accepted and clinically useful.

Probably the only point of general biological significance to emerge so far from studies of this kind is that the bulk of lymphoid neoplasias are of the B-cell rather than the T-cell series. Thus in man, although the T- and B-cell populations are probably present in approximately equal numbers, one might hazard a guess that the B-cell population has a more profound capacity for mitosis during which the various cumulative errors, involved in the generation of a malignant behaviour pattern, may have the chance to accumulate.

## REFERENCES

1. Claman, H.N., Chaperon, E.A., Triplett, R.F.: Thymus-marrow cell combinations. Synergism in antibody production. Proc. Soc. Exp. Biol. (N.Y.) 122, 1167 (1966)
2. Davies, A.J.S., Leuchars, E., Wallis, V., Marchant, R., Elliott, E.V.: The failure of thymus-derived cells to produce antibody. Transplantation 5, 222 (1967)
3. Mitchell, G.F., Miller, J.F.A.P.: Cell to cell interaction in the immune response. II. The source of hemolysin-forming cells in irradiated mice given bone marrow and thymus or thoracic duct lymphocytes. J. exp. Med. 128, 821 (1968)
4. Raff, M.C.: Two dictinct populations of periphral lymphocytes in mice distinguishable by immunofluorescence. Immunol. 19, 637 (1970)
5. Greaves, M.F., Owen, J.J.T., Raff, M.C.: T and B lymphocytes. Amsterdam: Excerpta Medica and New York: Elsevier (1973)
6. Papamichail, M., Brown, J.C., Holborow, E.J.: Immunoglobulins on the surface of human lymphocytes. Lancet 2, 850 (1971)
7. Stathopoulos, G., Elliott, E.V.: Formation of mouse or sheep red-blood-cell rosettes by lymphocytes from normal and leukaemic individuals. Lancet 1, 600 (1974)
8. Stathopoulos, G., Papamichail, M., Sheldon, P., Catovsky, D., Davies, A.J.S., Holborow, E.J., Wiltshaw, E.: Immunological studies in a case of T-cell leukaemia. J. clin. Pathol. 27, 851 (1974)
9. Dickler, H.B., Siegal, F.P., Bentwich, Z.H., Kunkel, H.G.: Lymphocyte binding of aggregated IgG and surface Ig staining in chronic lymphocytic leukaemia. Clin. exp. Immunol. 14, 97 (1973)
10. Lille, I., Desplaces, A., Meens, L., Saracino, R.T.: Thymus-derived profilerating lymphocytes in chronic lymphocytic leukaemia. Lancet 2, 263 (1973)

# Chapter 4

# In vitro Interactions Between Tumor Cells and Immune Lymphoid Cells

J. P. LEVY, E. GOMARD, A. SENIK, and J. C. LECLERC

In the past 6 years after the very important initial contribution of
HELLSTRÖM (11), about 100 papers have been published, reporting the
existence of tumor-specific, cell-mediated immune reactions (CMIR) in
man. Now, in the last 2 years, several groups have clearly demonstrated
that most, and perhaps all, of these results are not related to the
anti-tumor response, since they also exist in controls at the same level
and with the same frequency (3, 5, 20, 29). In fact, no attention has
been given to the nature of the effector cell or to their specificity
in many of the experiments reported. Perhaps it is useful to return
to clear experimental models to try to etablish the significance of the
in vitro methods used in investigations on cell-mediated antitumor
immunity, and to determine whether the anti-tumor immune response is
actually a response against the tumor or in fact an intercurrent phenomenon.

The murine sarcoma virus (MSV) system is interesting for several reasons: it allows the study of the reactions during the development of an
autochthonous primary tumor, the comparison of regressors and progres-
sors, and it is characterized by the existence of several different
well-defined antigens at the tumor cell surface. Furthermore, this system has been studied by several groups, which have used all the available
methods in cellular immunology. Some of the more important studies in
this field are summarized in Table 1. Table 2 analyzes the main characteristics of the different methods. It is important to emphasize that
some methods, such as the proline assay (PA) (2) and the microcytotoxicity assay (MA), use sarcoma cells in monolayers as targets, whereas
other methods use lymphoma cells in suspensions which are supposed to
be antigenically related. Another point is that the methods which measure cytolysis evidence T effector cells whereas the cytostasis assay
(CA) (4) is a macrophage-mediated phenomenon (15, 26). Non-T cells are
also responsive for the cytostasis part of the MA (16, 21, 24). In
correlation, it appears that a good antigenic specificity exists only
when T-cell-mediated immune cytolysis at the exclusion of any cytostasis
is measured.

In fact, when tumor and immune lymphoid cells are mixed in vitro several
different phenomena occur simultaneously, which cannot be separated
by the MA, but which are easily analyzed by more precise methods. Aliquots of the same lymphoid and target cell mixtures have been studied
in the chromium release test (CRT) (17, 19), in the CA (26), and in
the recently described secondary CRT (S.CRT) (27), which allows the
secondary antitumor response to be measured, with in vitro activation
of cytolytic T-lymphocytes (CTL). The experimental conditions were
the same in all three tests except that: (a) CRT was determined during
the first few hours by adding chromium-labeled target cells just at
the beginning of the incubation period, (b) S.CRT was determined by
adding identical target cells in the coculture on day 3, and (c) CA was

Table 1

Main methods to detect the cell-mediated immune reaction in the MSV system.

A.  RECOGNITION OF THE TUMOR CELL ANTIGENS

 1.  Mixed leucocyte tumor cell reaction (MLTR) SENIK et al. 1973; GORCZYNSKI 1974

 2.  Macrophage migration inhibition test (MMIT) HALLIDAY et al. 1971

B.  IN VITRO INHIBITION OF THE TUMOR CELL GROWTH

 3.  Colony inhibition test (CIT) and the microcytotoxocity assay (MA): HELLSTRÖM et al. 1969; LAMON
     et al. 1973; PLATA et al. 1974; SEEGER et al. 1974.

C.  IN VITRO CYTOLYSIS OF TUMOR CELLS

 4.  Chromium release test (CRT): LECLERC et al. 1972-1973; PLATA et al. 1974; LAVRIN et al. 1972;
     GORCZYNSKI and KNIGHT 1975.

 5.  Microcytotoxicity assay with $^3$H-proline labeled target cells (PA): GOMARD et al. 1976.

D.  IN VITRO CYTOSTASIS OF TUMOR CELLS

 6.  Cytostasis assay (CA): SENIK et al. 1974.

E.  IN VITRO STIMULATION OF CYTOLYTIC EFFECTOR CELLS

 7.  Cell-mediated lymphocytotoxicity (CML): PLATA et al. 1975; SENIK et al. 1975

Table 2. MSV tumor system: Comparison of the different in vitro methods which are supposed to test the effector cells of the anti-tumor reaction

| | Target cells | Effector cells | Cytolysis | Cytostasis | Blocking by progressor sera | Antigenic specificities |
|---|---|---|---|---|---|---|
| MA | Sarcoma cells | T and non-T (B? macrophages) | + | + | + | Poor |
| CRT | Lymphoma cells | T | + | − | − | Good |
| CA | Lymphoma cells | Macrophages | − | + | + | Poor |
| PA | Sarcoma cells | T | + | − | ? | Good |
| CML | Targets are lymphoma cells but the in vitro stimulation can be done by all kinds of cells | T | + | − | ? | Good |

determined at the same time by measuring the incorporation of $^3$H-thym-idine in the 3-day cocultivated tumor cells.

From the results four different points arose for consideration: (a) On the first day a strong CTL-mediated cytolysis occured due to the CTL which were already present in vivo in the donor mice, as described previously (19). (b) All the target cells are not destroyed, and after 2 days a population relatively resistant to the immune cytolysis has been selected. The same would be true even in the absence of CTL in the culture (26). (c) Tumor cells in vitro stimulate the T cells to maintain and even strongly increase the CTL activity of the whole cul-ture (27). On the other hand, in the absence of stimulating tumor cells the CTL activity rapidly decreases. Macrophages play a role in the stimulation but they are not the effector cells (27). This increased activity of CTL is in opposition with the decreased sensitivity of tumor cells, so that it can be relatively masked if the cytolysis is measured with the initially cultured tumor cells. However, it is easily demon-strated when freshly sampled $^{51}$Cr-labeled ascitic cells are added to the culture on day 3, as was performed in the S. CRT (27). (d) During incubation non-T cells, which are mainly macrophages, are activated by the interaction of immune lymphoid cells and tumor cells, but the activation is nonspecific. They exert a nonspecific cytostasis on the cultivated tumor cells, as shown by the CA (15, 26). A weak specific cytostatic affect could perhaps also exist (26), but it is a minor com-ponent in the usual conditions of the tests.

These results allow us to determine the respective advantages of the different methods used for testing CMIR in the MSV tumor system.

a. The CRT can be used to determine whether an animal possesses specific CTL at a given moment. However, the nature of the effector cells must be precise in every system, since under the same experimental conditions, the CRT may reveal nonspecific cytolysis due to non-T cells as demonstra-ted in AKR preleukemic mice (6) and in nonleukemic strains of mice (13).

b. The proline assay (PA) tests a very similar phenomenon, T dependent and cytolytic (7). However, it has some additional advantages: the possibility of using sarcoma cells in monolayer as targets, and to in-crease the incubation period, because the spontaneous release of pro-line is far less important than the chromium release. For these reasons, the test appears more sensitive and it seems to be possibly more valu-able in the study of the involved antigenic specificities at the sur-face of sarcoma cells (7).

c. The cell-mediated lymphocytotoxicity (CML) (23) and the S. CRT (27) which test the same secondary response, are useful for measuring the potential ability to mount a CTL response. As CML is more sensitive it is probably more valuable in this aim. On the othe hand, S. CRT, which is very simple to perform, very specific, and yields reproducible re-sults, is a very useful method for testing the antigenic specificity which is involved in the CMIR.

d. The CA is mainly concerned with the measurement of the nonspecific cytostatic non-T cell reaction (15, 24, 26).

e. The classical MA offers a more difficult interpretation of results and reflects the complexity of immune response with several kinds of effector cell populations and blocking and unblocking factors. A large part of the reaction is nonspecific. MA needs more analytical methods for further investigations. However, this assay has been most extensive-ly used in human research during the past 6 years.

On the whole, a critical study of the significance of the method which are used in vitro to measure CMIR in the MSV system, allows us to understand most of the discrepancies reported in the results of the different groups. Although these problems cannot be expanded on here three points should be briefly noted:

1. Different kinetics of the antitumor cell response have been described (8, 9, 10, 15, 18, 21, 25, 26). They are due to the fact that the various methods do not test the same reaction and perhaps the same antigens on different target cells.

2. The antigens which are involved in the in vitro reactions are not clearly defined. For some groups, antigens due to derepressed endogenous virus are mainly involved (12), for other groups, specific antigens probably related to the P30 viral polypeptides may play a major role (9). In our experience, the FMRGi antigen appears very important both in vivo and in vitro, and it is clear that the ability to produce viruses is a very important point in the determination of cell antigenicity in vitro (28). However, these results are not necessarily contradictory: from our recent results obtained in PA, S. CRT, and in vivo protection, it appears that different T-cell populations, with probably different antigenic specificities are present and play some role both in vivo and in vitro in the MSV system. One of the specificities involved is probably of the FMRGi type, but other additional antigens, notably a possible sarcoma-specific antigen, are also involved (7). It is very possible that the P30 associated antigens (9) or a sarcoma-specific antigen as described by AOKI et al. (1) or endogenous virus specific antigen (12) or an embryonic antigen (30) which also exist on these cells could play some role and we have arguments that indicate that at least two, and perhaps three or more antigens are simultaneously concerned.

3. Discrepancies have been reported in the blocking of T cells by soluble antigens. We observed blocking in MA but not in CRT (22), although blocking was observed in a CRT variant using sarcoma cells as target (9). This is in good agreement with our observations that different antigens are simultaneously involved in the reactions, but very probably are not equally represented on sarcoma cells and lymphoma cells (7).

In conclusion, the comparison of the different methods opens the possibility to determine the different target antigens in the CMIR we observed in vitro, and hence to a comparison with in vivo tumor rejection. There is no doubt that the in vivo relevance of the in vitro reactions is now the main problem to be solved.

As a model for human tumors, the MSV system indicates at least that the in vitro detection of a CMIR is not sufficient to draw definite conclusions. In every case the first prerequisite must be to determine: (a) the effector cells, (b) their mode of action, and (c) their antigenic specificities.

REFERENCES

1. Aoki, T., Stephenson, J.R., Aaronson, S.A., Hau, K.C.: Surface antigens of mammalian sarcoma virus-transformed non producer cells. Proc. Nat. Acad. Sci. USA 71, 3445 (1974)
2. Bean, M.A., Pees, M., Rosen, G., Oettgen, H.F.: Prelabeling target cells with $^3$H-proline as a method for studying lymphocyte cytotoxicity. Nat. Cancer Inst. Monograph 37, 41 (1973)

3. Bloom, E.T., Ossorio, R.C., Brosman, S.A.: Cell-mediated cytotoxicity against human bladder cancer. Int. J. Cancer 14, 326 (1974)
4. Chia, E., Festenstein, H.: Specific cytostatic effect of lymph node from normal and T-cell deficient mice on syngeneic tumor target cells in vitro and its specific abrogation by body fluids from syngeneic tumor-bearing mice. Europ. J. Immunol. 3, 483 (1973)
5. De Vries, J.E., Cornain, S., Rumke, P.: Cytotoxicity of non-T versus T-lymphocytes from melanoma patient and healthy donors on short and long term cultured melanoma cells. Int. J. Cancer 14, 427 (1974)
6. Gomard, E., Leclerc, J.C., Levy, J.P.: Spontaneous anti lymphoma reaction of preleukaemic AKR mice: a non-T cell killing. Nature 250, 671 (1974)
7. Gomard, E., Henin, Y., Levy, J.P.: Target antigens in the cell mediated anti-tumor in vitro reactions in the MSV system. I. Antigens detected on sarcoma cells by the proline assay. To be published 1976
8. Gorczynski, R.M.: Immunity to murine sarcoma virus induced tumors. I. Specific T lymphocytes active in MMI and lymphocyte transformation. J. Immunol. 112, 1815 (1974)
9. Gorczynski, R.M., Knight, R.A.: Immunity to murine sarcoma virus induced tumours. IV. Direct cellular cytolysis of $^{51}$Cr labeled tart cells in vitro and analysis of blocking factors which modulate cytotoxicity. Brit. J. Cancer 31, 387 (1975)
10. Halliday, W.J.: Blocking effect of serum from tumor bearing animals on macrophage migration inhibition with tumor antigens. J. Immunol. 106, 855 (1971)
11. Hellström, I., Hellström, K.E.: Studies on cellular immunity and its serum-mediated inhibition in Moloney-virus induced mouse sarcomas. Int. J. Cancer 4, 587 (1969)
12. Herberman, R.B., Aoki, T., Nunn, M., Lavrin, D.H., Soares, N., Gazdar, A., Holden, H., Chang, K.S.S.: Specificity of $^{51}$Cr release cytotoxicity of lymphocytes immune to murine sarcoma virus. J. Nat. Cancer Inst. 53, 1103 (1974)
13. Herberman, R.B., Nunn, M.E., Holden, H.T., Lavrin, D.H.: Natural cytotoxic reactivity of mouse lymphoid cells against syngeneic and allogeneic tumors. II. Characterization of effector cells. Int. J. Cancer 16, 230 (1975)
14. Kiessling, R., Klein, E., Pross, H., Wigzell, H.: "Natural" killer cells in the mouse. II. Cytotoxic cells with specificity for mouse Moloney leukemia cells. Characteristics of the killer cells. Europ. J. Immunol. 5, 117 (1975)
15. Kirchner, H., Muchmore, A.V., Chused, T.M., Holden, H.T., Herberman, R.B.: Imhibition of proliferation of lymphoma cells and T lymphocytes by suppressor cells from spleen of tumor bearing mice. J. Immunol. 114, 206 (1975)
16. Lamon, E.W., Skurzak, H.M., Klein, E., Wigzell, H.: In vitro cytotoxicty by a non thymus processed lymphocyte population with specificity for a virally determined tumor cell surface antigen. J. Exp. Med. 136, 1072 (1972)
17. Lavrin, D.H., Herberman, R.B., Nunn, M, Soares, N.: In vitro cytotoxicity studies of murine sarcoma virus-induced immunity in mice. J. Nat. Cancer Inst. 51, 1497 (1973)
18. Leclerc, J.C., Gomard, E., Levy, J.P.: Cell-mediated reaction against tumors induced by oncornaviruses. I. Kinetics and specificity of the immune response in murine sarcoma virus (MSV) induced tumors and transplanted lymphomas. Int. J. Cancer 10, 589 (1972)
19. Leclerc, J.C., Gomard, E., Plata, F., Levy, J.P.: Cell-mediated immune reaction against tumors induced by oncornaviruses. II. Nature of the effector cells in tumor cell cytolysis. Int. J. Cancer 11, 426 (1973)

20. Peter, H., Pavie-Fisher, J., Fridman, W.H., Aubert, C., Cesarini, C., Roubin, R., Kourilsky, F.M.: Cell-mediated cytotoxicity in vitro of normal human lymphocyte against tissue culture melanoma cell line (IGR 3). J. Immunol. 115, 539 (1975)

21. Plata, F., Gomard, E., Leclerc, J.C., Levy, J.P.: Comparative in vitro studies on effector cell diversity in the cellular immunity to murine sarcoma virus (MSV)-induced tumors in mice. J. Immunol. 112, 1477 (1974)

22. Plata, F., Levy, J.P.: Blocking of syngeneic effector T cells by soluble tumour antigens. Nature 249, 272 (1974)

23. Plata, F., Cerottini, J.C., Brummer, K.T.: Primary and secondary in vitro generation of cytolytic T lymphocytes in the murine sarcoma virus system. Europ. J. Immunol. 5, 227 (1975)

24. Seeger, R.C., Rayner, S,A., Owen, J.J.T.: An analysis of variables affecting the measurement of tumor immunity in vitro with 125I-iodo-deoxyuridine labeled target cells. Studies of immunity to primary Moloney sarcomas. Int. J. Cancer 13, 697 (1974)

25. Senik, A., Gomard, E., Plata, F., Levy, J.P.: Cell-mediated immune reaction against tumors induced by oncornaviruses. III. Studies by mixed lymphocyte. Tumor reaction. Int. J. Cancer 12, 233 (1973)

26. Senik, A., De Giorgi, L., Levy, J.P.: Cell-mediated anti-tumor immunity in oncornaviruses-induced tumors: specific cytostasis of tumor cells by spleen and lymph node cells. Int. J. Cancer 14, 386 (1974)

27. Senik, A., Pozzo-Hebrero, F., Levy, J.P.: Secondary specific immune response in vitro to MSV tumor cells. Int. J. Cancer 16, 946 (1975)

28. Senik, A., Gisselbrecht, S., Levy, J.P.: Antigenic specificities of the cell-mediated anti-tumor reactions in the MSV system studied by the secondary chromium release test. Int. J. Cancer 16, 960 (1975)

29. Takasugi, M., Mickey, M.R., Terasaki, P.J.: Reactivity of lymphocyte from normal persons on cultured tumor cells. Cancer Res. 33, 2898 (1973)

30. Ting, C.C., Shin, C., Rodrigues, D., Herberman, R.B.: Cell-mediated immunity to Friend virus induced leukemias. Cancer Res. 34, 1684 (1974)

# Chapter 5

# Activation and Cytotoxic Activity of Macrophages: A Short Review

J. MAUEL

## 1. ON THE DEFINITION OF THE ACTIVATED STATE

Resistance to certain infections is critically dependent on the acquisition by host macrophages of properties not expressed by normal cells,
among which one notes an increased capacity to destroy intracellular
microorganisms (4, 35, 41). In this particular state, macrophages are
said to be "activated". NELSON (43) suggested that the term "activated"
should be applied only to cells capable of increased microbicidal
capacity. However, evidence that macrophages stimulated in various ways
can exert cytotoxic or cytostatic effects on different types of nonmicrobial target cells has accumulated recently, and it has also become
customary to designate the term "activated" to the cells which display
these newly discovered properties. In the context of this paper, the
activated macrophage will thus be defined as a cell endowed with the
capacity to destroy (or restrict the growth of), in an immunologically
nonspecific way, microbial and/or nonmicrobial targets. This definition
does not mean that the mechanisms operating against different targets
are identical, nor does it imply that a given population of activated
macrophages should necessarily manifest both properties (destruction
of microbial and nonmicrobial targets); different types of activation
may occur which could differ not only on a quantitative, but also on
a qualitative basis.

Activation in its strict sense, on the other hand, is accompanied by
modifications of macrophage physiology (9), such as increased metabolic
activity that can be measured in a variety of tests. The correlation
between these modifications and the newly acquired properties mentioned
above are uncertain, however, and the term "stimulation" is to be pre-
ferred when reference is made to biochemical or morphological alterations in the absence of formal proof of increased cytotoxic properties
(43).

## 2. MECHANISMS OF ACTIVATION

A large variety of stimuli can elicit the appearance in macrophages
of the specific functions linked to the expression of the activated
state. Two broad classes of activating mechanisms have been distinguished (11): those where activation results from the immunologically
specific interaction between sensitized lymphocytes and antigen ("specific activation"), and those where activation does not appear to have
an immunological basis ("nonspecific activation").

These terms are somewhat misleading. Firstly, even "specific" activation seems to occur as a two-step mechanism where the second step is non-specific. Secondly, it should be remenbered that, even in the case of specific activation, the expression of the activated state (destruction of microorganisms and/or nonmicrobial target cells) appears to have no immunological specificity (cf. below).

## 2.1. Specific Activation

Extensive experimentation on the mechanisms of recovery from various bacterial and protozoal infections strongly suggests that specific activation occurs as a result of interaction between microbial antigen and specifically sensitized cells of the T lineage (30, 36, 44); the stimulated lymphocytes then appear to release nonspecific soluble factors (17, 29) (lymphokines) which in turn activate macrophages. An important implication of these findings is that some degree of macrophage activation probably accompanies every cell-mediated reaction, even if it remains unrecognized due to the apparent absence of a functional role for such an event (except in the obvious case of the destruction of microorganisms). Whether macrophage activation in cell-mediated reactions serves another, as yet unrecognized, purpose, such as contributing to a homeostatic mechanism, remains to be determined (cf. Section 3.2).

An entirely different mechanism of specific activation has been described based on the following findings: macrophages from animals immunized against syngeneic or allogeneic tumor cells display a specific cytotoxic activity, i.e., they are capable of restricting the growth of, or of destroying, target cells of the genotype used for immunization, but not cells from an unrelated origin (12, 31). This implies a mechanism whereby macrophages can recognize target antigens in an immunologically specific manner, presumably by some "recognition structures" on their surface. The nature of these structures is still unknown, but might be different from classical immunoglobulins, since the effect of such "immune" macrophages is not affected by anti-Ig serum (13).

Other experiments suggest that a similar specific activity can be induced in normal macrophages by co-cultivation with lymphoid cells from immune animals (12), or with supernatants from such cells stimulated by the specific antigen, and containing a "specific macrophage arming factor" (SMAF) (15) or "macrophage cytotoxicity factor" (MCF) (33), apparently derived from T cells.

Macrophages with specific cytotoxic activity originating from in vivo immunization, or in vitro induction, are said to be "armed". Armed macrophages can be led to a truly activated state by exposure to the specific target cell (14); this renders them nonspecifically cytostatic for other kinds of cells, unrelated to the specific one. In this case, activation seems to be a two-step mechanism, the first one (arming) mediated by T-lymphocytes, the second one (activation) occuring as a result of interaction between armed macrophages and antigen. For additional information on the effect of armed macrophages see Section 3.4.

## 2.2. Non-Specific Activation

In vitro T-cell stimulation by mitogens, or in mixed lymphocyte cultures, will induce macrophages to destroy intracellular microorganisms and nonmicrobial target cells (18, 24, 37). In all these instances, evidence is in favor of a mechanism mediated by lymphokines released from the stimulated lymphocytes.

Other stimuli will induce nonspecific macrophage activation in vivo
or in vitro. Such is the case with endotoxin (1, 41),double-stranded
RNA (1, 2) , and bacterial phospholipidic extract (BPE) (16); whether
some of these agents act at the level of the macrophage itself, as
suggested by in vitro experiments, is still uncertain, as the contribution of lymphocytes is difficult to exclude formally.

Finally, procedures used to induce macrophages in the peritoneal cavity
of experimental animals, such as injecting mild irritants (starch,
peptone, etc.) have been shown to produce activated cells (26). The
mechanism of this activation is unknown.

The multiplicity of the mechanisms of macrophage activation indicates
that this biological phenomenon is of vital importance to the host. In
addition, the acquisition of activated functions in the apparent absence
of lymphocyte-mediated mechanisms suggests that, during the course of
evolution, macrophage activation may have preceded the development of
an immune apparatus as a mechanism of protection against external or
internal invaders.


3. EFFECT OF ACTIVATED AND ARMED MACROPHAGES ON TARGET CELLS


Depending on the type of target considered, three different effects
have been described: (a) intracellular killing and digestion, (b) growth
inhibition, and (c) extracellular lysis. No adequate data exist as to
the relationship between these three types of effects. Macrophages from
chronically infected animals (20, 47), or normal macrophages exposed
in vitro to mitogen-stimulated lymphocytes, may be cytocidal for both
intracellular microorganisms and tumor cells (Figs. 1 and 2). However,
it is not known whether macrophages that are activated to destroy
microorganisms will invariably affect nonmicrobial cells, and vice
versa.

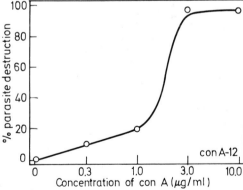

*Fig. 1. Killing of intracellular microorganisms by activated macropha-
ges. Monolayers of starch-induced CBA mouse peritoneal macrophages were
infected in vitro with the intracellular protozoan parasite Leishmania
enriettii. Infected macrophages were then activated by cocultivation
with syngeneic lymphocytes in presence of various concentrations of
Concanavalin A (Con A). Parasite destruction was measured after 48 h
of activation, following the technique described by MAUEL et al. (38)*

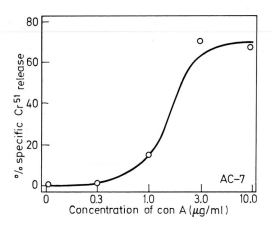

Fig. 2. *Destruction of tumor cells by activated macrophages. Starch-induced CBA mouse peritoneal macrophages were activated in vitro by cocultivation with syngeneic lymphocytes in presence of various concentrations of Concanavalin A (Con A). After 48 h of activation, the macrophage monolayers were extensively washed; $^{51}$Cr-labeled P-815 mastocytoma cells (of DBA-2 genotype) were then added. Specific chromium release was measured after 10 h of contact between activated macrophages and target cells*

## 3.1. Effect of Activated Macrophages on Intracellular Microorganisms

As mentioned above (cf. Section 2.1) the effect of activated macrophages on microorganisms appears to have no immunological specificity, even when the activating mechanism proceeds from an immunological reaction. Thus, macrophages activated in the course of an immune response to Bacillus Calmette-Guérin (BCG) infection will destroy not only BCG, but also unrelated microorganisms such as Listeria monocytogenes (36). Similarly, macrophage activation in vitro following the specific interaction of sensitized lymphocytes with nonmicrobial antigen will result in the destruction of microorganisms with no relationship to the activating stimulus (38, 49).

The effect of activated macrophages on intracellular microorganisms is one of growth inhibition or lysis, the nature of the effect being dependent on both the magnitude of the activated state and the nature of the microorganism considered as the target (3, 38). FOWLES et al. (17) described a bacteriostatic effect of macrophages activated by supernatants of stimulated lymphocytes, whereas SIMON and SHEAGREN (49), using the same target, reported a true killing activity of macrophages exposed directly to sensitized lymphocytes in the presence of antigen. As discussed by D'ARCY HART (19), great care must be exercised in the evaluation and comparison of data from different investigators, as varying test conditions may considerably influence the outcome of the experiments. Under suitable conditions, macrophage activation can lead to the complete destruction of intracellular parasites within short time periods (Fig. 1).

Whether activated macrophages take part in the defence against metazoan parasites, by cytocidal processes not involving phagocytosis, is still unknown. Recent results by CAPRON et al. (7), using an experimental model in the rat, suggest that macrophages coated with IgE antibody may attach to and be deleterious for Schistosoma mansoni, although no information is given as to the possible "activated" nature of the macrophages under study.

## 3.2. Effect of Activated Macrophages on Normal Cells

There seems to be good evidence from the work of KELLER (26) that activated macrophages inhibit the growth in vitro of rapidly proliferating
normal cells; this effect, however, is observed only when sensitive
techniques based on the measurement of incorporation of DNA precusors
are used. Little or no effect of any type is observed when the target
cell is growing slowly. It has been repeatedly emphasized by several
groups (cf. 51) that no actual destruction of normal cells occurs, as
opposed to the cytotoxic effect of activated macrophages on neoplastic
targets (cf. below).

A special case of target cells is the lymphocyte. Many investigators
have reported a modulation by macrophages, or macrophage products, of
lymphocyte mitogenic response to PHA and other stimuli (6, 48, 50, 52).
Stimulated macrophages appear to be particularly effective in this
respect (42). The possibility that such an effect could be interpreted
as a regulatory mechanism of lymphocyte proliferation is extremely
appealing.

## 3.3. Effect of Activated Macrophages on Tumor Cells

A striking effect of activated macrophages, as reported by several
investigators, is the capacity of these cells not only to inhibit the
growth of, but to actually destroy neoplastic targets by immunologically
nonspecific mechanisms (20, 22, 23, 26, 46). Using appropriate targets,
this effect can be easily demonstrated by measuring $^{51}Cr$ release from
labeled tumor cells in contact with activated macrophages (Fig. 2).

The lytic effect of activated macrophages appears to be slower than
that obtained using specifically sensitized lymphocytes under optimal
conditions, where complete destruction of the target cells can be
achieved within less than 2 h (8). However, this may be due to different
geometrical parameters of the two test systems rather than to activated
macrophages being actually less efficient than lymphocytes.

As mentioned above, it appears that activated macrophages only inhibit
the growth of normal cells whereas they seem to affect the viability
of tumor cells. If confirmed, this capacity of activated macrophages
to distinguish cells with abnormal growth properties from their normal
counterparts constitutes the most remarkable feature of their cytotoxic
effect. Although the mechanisms underlying this capacity to discriminate
tumor from normal cells is unknown, it has been linked with the fact
that tumor cells seem to possess modified surface features which can be
revealed by appropriate markers, such as plant lectins (5). Such changes
might reflect a  dedifferentiation process accompanied by the expression, at the surface level, of molecular archetypes common to all tumor
cells (cf. 51). Whether activated macrophages recognize tumor cells
by detecting such surface changes is, at the moment, entirely conjec-
tural.

## 3.4. Specificity vs. Nonspecificity, and the Case of the Armed Macro-
phage

As mentioned earlier, the armed macrophage is defined as a cell whose
cytotoxic effect is directed toward a specific target, as opposed to
the activated macrophage which, by definition, exerts its functions in
a nonspecific manner. One mechanism of arming, as reported by two different groups, consists of incubating normal peritoneal macrophages
with SMAF or MCF, obtained from the supernatant culture fluids of

reaction mixtures containing lymphocytes from animals immune to a syngeneic or allogeneic tumor, and the specific target cell. Such factors have been claimed to induce a cytotoxic activity in macrophages that is specific for the immunizing cell (underline{15}, underline{32}). However, it is still difficult to assess the validity of this contention, since the data have not been confirmed by other groups. Indeed, other investigators have used the same basic principle to produce truly activated macrophages with no specificity in their cytotoxic potential (underline{10}, underline{45}). In this case, the cytotoxic effect of macrophages would appear to be induced by "classical" lymphokines released by sensitized lymphocytes in contact with the specific target cell; the mechanism of activation would be expected to be similar to that observed following incubation of immune lymphocytes with microbial or other soluble antigens (underline{46}).

These two contradictory results deriving from the same experimental approach are, at the moment, difficult to reconcile, but some explanations may be offered. As discussed by LOHMANN-MATTHES et al. (underline{34}), differences may result from the techniques used to prepare macrophage monolayers for in vitro experimentation; in addition, both specific and nonspecific effects might occur concomitantly, but one of them may go unrecognized by lack of use of the proper test system. Thus cytostasis will not be detected by techniques measuring cell destruction (for instance, using $^{51}Cr$ release), and conversely, methods used to monitor cell growth will not be adequate for recording cytolysis.


## 4. MECHANISMS OF THE CYTOTOXIC ACTION OF ACTIVATED MACROPHAGES

### 4.1. Microbial Targets

A variety of morphologic and metabolic changes have been described in stimulated macrophages, including increased adherence to glass and plastic, increased membrane ruffling, increased or decreased phagocytic activity, increased hexose monophosphate shunt (HMPS), and increases or decreases of various enzyme levels (underline{9}). There is, at the present time, no data formally supporting the association of any of these parameters with the acquisition by activated macrophages of an enhanced microbicidal potential. Mechanisms have been proposed to explain bacterial destruction in polymorphonuclear leukocytes, based on a halogenation process utilizing $H_2O_2$ and cellular peroxidases (underline{28}). The relevance of this mechanism to the microbicidal effect of activated macrophages is not known, especially since mature macrophages, at least in the mouse, are thought to be relatively poor in peroxidase activity (underline{25}).


### 4.2. Nonmicrobial Targets

Activated macrophages appear to kill tumor cells by a nonphagocytic mechanism. Several authors have emphasized the need for a close contact between activated macrophages and target cells in order for the latter to be affected. However, a recent report by KELLER (underline{26}) suggests that, in addition to a contact-mediated effect, soluble factors produced by activated macrophages may decrease target-cell proliferation. In this context, it is interesting to note that activated macrophages have also been claimed to liberate a soluble factor with "sterilizing" properties against L.monocytogenes (underline{40}).

On contact with neoplastic target cells, translational movement of activated macrophages is increased considerably and macrophages appear to make repeated contacts of short duration (2 h) with target cells (underline{39}).

36

Cytostasis, followed by cytolysis, ensues. If cell to cell contact is required,what is the nature of the cytotoxic mechanism? In a series of interesting experiments, HIBBS (21) observed that activated macrophages appear to inject lysosomal constituents inside target cells; inhibitors of lysosome enzymes, such as trypan blue, did not prevent the passage of lysosomes from macrophages to target cells, but blocked subsequent cellular destruction, suggesting that lysosomal enzymes are important in effecting target-cell lysis. Slightly conflicting results have been obtained by KELLER et al. (27) who found no correlation between cytostasis and lysosomal enzyme levels.


## 5. SUMMARY AND CONCLUSIONS


Interaction of sensitized T-lymphocytes with specific antigen, as well as several other nonimmunological stimuli, will induce the appearance of new properties in macrophages collectively referred to as "activation". The importance of macrophage activation in various physiological processes is only just beginning to be understood. A growing body of evidence strongly suggests that activated macrophages may play a dual role: firstly in protecting the host against certain intracellular pathogens, and secondly in modulating cell proliferation and adversely affecting cells with abnormal growth properties. It is expected that the ability of activated macrophages to discriminate between normal and tumor cells will receive increasing attention. If confirmed, this property may be of major importance with regard to immunotherapy of tumors.

## REFERENCES


1. Alexander, P., Evans, R.: Endotoxin and double-stranded RNA render macrophages cytotoxic. Nature (New Biol.) 232, 76 (1971)
2. Araujo, F.G., Remington, J.S.: Protection against T. gondii in mice immunized with toxoplasma cell fractions, RNA and synthetic poly-ribonucleotides. Immunol. 27, 711 (1974)
3. Behin, R., Mauel, J., Biroum-Noerjasin, Rowe, D.S.: Mechanisms of protective immunity in experimental leishmaniasis. II. Selective destruction of different Leishmania species in activated guinea-pig and mouse macrophages. Clin. exp. Immunol. 20, 351 (1975)
4. Blanden, R.V.: Modification of macrophage function. R.E.S. J. Retic. Soc. 5, 179 (1968)
5. Burger, M.M., Martin, G.S.: Agglutination of cells transformed by Rous sarcoma virus by wheat germ agglutinin and concanavalin A. Nature (New Biol.) 237, 9 (1972)
6. Calderon, J., Unanue, E.R.: Two biological activities regulating cell proliferation found in cultures of peritoneal exudate cells. Nature 253, 359 (1975)
7. Capron, A., Dessaint, J.P., Capron, M., Bazin, H.: Specific IgE antibodies in immune adherence of normal macrophages to Schistosoma mansoni schitosomules. Nature 253, 474 (1975)
8. Cerottini, J.C., Brunner, K.T.: Cell-mediated cytotoxixity, allograft rejection and tumor immunity. Adv. Immunol. 18, 67 (1974)
9. David, J.R.: Macrophage activation induced by lymphocyte mediators. In: Karolinska Symposia on Research Methods in Reproductive Endocrinology. Copenhagen: Forum Printers, 1974, pp. 1-14

10. Dimitriu, A., Dy, M., Thompson, N., Hamburger, G.: Macrophage cytotoxicity in the mouse immune response against a skin allograft. J. Immunol. 114, 195 (1975)
11. Evans, R.: Specific and non-specific activation of macrophages. In: Activation of macrophages. Workshop Conference Hoechst. Wagner, W. and Hahn, H., Amsterdam and New York: 1974, Vol. II, pp. 304-313
12. Evans, R., Alexander, P.: Cooperation of immune lymphoid cells with macrophages in tumour immunity. Nature 228, 620 (1970)
13. Evans, R., Alexander, P.: Role of macrophages in tumour immunity. II. Involvement of a macrophage cytophylic factor during syngeneic tumour growth inhibition. Immunol. 23, 627 (1972a)
14. Evans, R., Alexander, P.: Mechanism of immunologically specific killing of tumour cells by macrophages. Nature 236, 168 (1972b)
15. Evans, R., Grant, C.K., Cox, H., Steele, K., Alexander, P.: Thymus-derived lymphocytes produce an immunologically specific macrophage arming factor. J. exp. Med. 136, 1318 (1972)
16. Fauve, R.M., Hevin, B.: Résistance paradoxale des souris thymoprives à l'injection par Listeria monocytogenes et Salmonelle typhimurium et action stimulante d'un extrait bactérien phospholipidique (EPB). C.R. Acad. Sc. Sér. D. 279, 1603 (1974)
17. Fowles, R.E., Fajardo, I.M., Leibowitch, J.L., David, J.R.: Enhancement of macrophage bacteriostasis by products of activated lymphocytes. J. exp. Med. 138, 952 (1973)
18. Godal, T., Rees, R.J.W., Lamvik, J.O.: Lymphocyte-mediated modification of blood-derived macrophage function in vitro; inhibition of growth of intracellular mycobacteria with lymphokines. Clin. exp. Immunol. 8, 625 (1971)
19. D'Arcy Hart, P.: Critical approach to the technique of assessment of antibacterial effects of activated mouse peritoniel macrophages. In: Activation of macrophages. Workshop Conference Hoechst, Wagner, W. and Hahn, H., Amsterdam and New York: 1974, Vol. II, pp. 131-137
20. Hibbs, J.B.: Macrophage non-immunologic recognition. Target cell factors related to contact inhibition. Science 180, 868 (1973)
21. Hibbs, J.B.: Heterocytolysis by macrophages activated by Bacillus-Calmette-Guérin: lysosome exocytosis in tumor cells. Science 184, 468 (1974)
22. Hibbs, J.B., Lambert, L.H., Remington, J.S.: Possible role of macrophage-mediated non-specific cytotoxicity in tumour resistance. Nature (New Biol.) 235, 48 (1972)
23. Holtermann, O.A., Djerassi, I., Lisafeld, B.A., Elias, E.G., Papermaster, B.W., Klein, E.: In vitro destruction of tumor cells by human monocytes. Proc. Soc. 147, 446 (1974)
24. Jones, T., Youmans, G.P.: Non-specific inhibition of growth of intracellular Listeria monocytogenes by lymphocyte culture products. Inf. Immun. 9, 472 (1974)
25. Karnovsky, M.L., Simmons, S., Glass, E.A., Shafer, A.W., D'Arcy Hart, P.: Metabolism of macrophages. In: Mononuclear Phagocytes, 103-117. Van Furth, Oxford and Edinburgh: Blackwell 1970
26. Keller, R.: Modulation of cell proliferation by macrophages: a possible function apart from cytotoxic tumour rejection. Brit. J. Cancer 30, 401 (1974)
27. Keller, R., Keist, R., Ivatt, R.J.: Functional and biochemical parameters of activation related to macrophage cytostatic effects on tumor cells. Int. J. Cancer 14, 675 (1974)
28. Klebanoff, S.J.: Iodination of bacteria. A bactericidal mechanism. J. exp. Med. 126, 1063 (1967)
29. Krahenbuhl, J.L., Remington, J.S.: In vitro induction of non-specific resistance in macrophages by specifically sensitized lymphocytes. Infec. Immun. 4, 337 (1971)

30. Lane, F.C., Unanue, E.R.: Requirement of thymus (T) lymphocytes for resistance to Listeriosis. J. exp. Med. 135, 1104 (1972)
31. Lohmann-Matthes, M.L., Schipper, H., Fischer, H.: Macrophage-mediated cytotoxicity against allogeneic target cells in vitro. Europ. J. Immunol. 2, 45 (1972)
32. Lohmann-Matthes, M.L., Fischer, H.: T-cell cytotoxicity and amplification of the cytotoxic reaction by macrophages. Transpl. Rev. 17, 150 (1973)
33. Lohmann-Matthes, M.L., Ziegler, F.G., Fischer, H.: Macrophage cytotoxicity factor. A product of in vitro sensitized thymus-dependent cells. Europ. J. Immunol. 3, 56 (1973)
34. Lohmann-Matthes, M.L., Ziegler, F.G., Ritter, G.: In vitro macrophage-mediated cytotoxicity in an allogeneic mouse system. In: Activation of macrophages, Workshop Conference Hoechst. Wagner, W. and Hahn, H. (eds.). Amsterdam and New York: Excerpta Medica 1974, Vol. II, pp. 293-304
35. Mackaness, G.B.: Cellular resistance to infection. J. exp. Med. 116, 381 (1962)
36. Mackaness, G.B.: The influence of immunologically commited lymphoid cells on macrophage activity in vivo. J. exp. Med. 129, 973 (1969)
37. Mauel, J., Biroum-Noerjasin, Behin, R.: Killing of intracellular parasites as a measure of amcrophage activation. In: Activation of macrophages, Workshop Conferences Hoechst, Wagner, W. and Hahn, H. (eds.). Amsterdam and New York: Excerpta Medica 1974, Vol. II, pp. 260-266
38. Mauel, J., Behin, R., Biroum-Noerjasin and Rowe, D.S.: Mechanisms of protective immunity in experimental cutaneous leishmaniasis of the Guinea-pig. I. Lack of effects of immune lymphocytes and of activated macrophages. Clin. exp. Immunol. 20, 339 (1975)
39. Melzer, M.L., Tucker, R.W., Breuer, A.C.: Interaction of BCG-activated macrophages with neoplastic and non-neoplastic cell lines in vitro: cinemicrographic analysis. Cell. Immunol. 17, 30 (1975)
40. Middlerbrook, G., Salmon, B.J., Kreisberg, J.J.: Sterilization of Listeria monocytogenes by Guinea-pig peritoneal exudate cell cultures. Cell. Immunol. 14, 270 (1974)
41. Nelson, D.S.: Macrophages as effectors of cell-mediated immunity. C.R.C. Critical Rev. in Microbiol. 1, 353 (1972)
42. Nelson, D.S.: Production by stimulated macrophages of factors depressing lymphocyte transformation. Nature 246, 306 (1973)
43. Nelson, D.S.: Immunity to infection, allograft immunity and tumor immunity: parallels and contrasts. Transpl. Rev. 19, 226 (1974)
44. North, R.: Cellular mediators of anti-listeria immunity as a enlarged population of short-lived, replicating T cells. Kinetics of their production. J. exp. Med. 138, 342 (1973)
45. Pfizenmaier, K., Trostmann, H., Röllinghoff, M., Wagner, H.: Cell-mediated allograft responses in vitro: VI. Studies on macrophage-mediated cytotoxicity. Immunol. 29, 967 (1975)
46. Piessens, W.F., Churchill, W.H., David, J.R.: Macrophage activated in vitro with lymphocyte mediators kill neoplastic but not normal cells. J. Immunol. 114, 293 (1975)
47. Remington, J.S., Krahenbuhl, J.L., Mendenhall, J.W.: A role for activated macrophages in resistance to infection with toxoplasma. Infec. Immunity 6, 829 (1972)
48. Scott, M.T.: Biological effects of the adjuvant Corynebacterium parvum. II. Evidence for macrophage-T cell interaction. Cell. Immunol. 5, 469 (1972)
49. Simon, H.B., Sheagren, J.N.: Cellular immunity in vitro. I. Immunologically mediated enhancement of macrophage bactericidal capacity. J. exp. Med. 133, 1377 (1971)

50. Sjöberg, O.: Effect of allogeneic cell interaction on the primary immune response in vitro. Cell types involved in suppression and stimulation of antibody synthesis. Clin. exp. Immunol. <u>12</u>, 365 (1972)
51. Smith, R., Landy, M.: Immunobiology of the tumor-host relationship. New York, San Francisco and London: Academic Press 1975, p. 125
52. Waldman, S.R., Gottlieb, A.A.: Macrophage regulation of DNA synthesis in lymphoid cells: effects of a soluble factor from macrophages. Cell. Immunol. <u>9</u>, 142 (1973)

# Chapter 6
# Cell-Membrane Activation of Macrophage Function

P. C. WILKINSON

## MACROPHAGE ACTIVATION

During the lifetime of any cell, the cell's activity varies from one
time to the next as the function which it serves are called on by the
body. Since cells are complex and have multiple functions, it is unlike-
ly that changes in one function necessarily occur synchronously with
changes in other functions. It is therefore apparent that to speak of
"activation" of cells is imprecise unless the function which is activated is precisely defined. This has led to some confusion in the
macrophage field, where the cells concerned are motile, phagocytic, capable of differentiation and mitosis, and active in both non-specific
and specific immune reactions. The term "activated" is most frequently
and most acceptably used to refer to a population of macrophages found
in vivo under certain experimental conditions, e.g. following injection of Bacillus Calmette-Guérin (BCG) or other stimulants, which, compared to control populations, show enhanced cytotoxic activity, for
example against bacteria such as Listeria spp. (25) or against tumour
cells (2) or in graft-versus-host reactions (11). These activated macrophages also frequently show other changes, e.g. an increase in phagocytic activity and an increased tendency to spread on substrata (28) or
increased metabolic activity (10). Population of macrophages which
show enhanced cytotoxic activity may be obtained from experimental animals one to three or more weeks after administration of suspensions of
certain bacteria such as Bordetella pertussis or Mycobacterium tuberculosis and related species. The enhancement of cytotoxic activity in
macrophages has been related to the presence of a specific immune response, chiefly of the cell-mediated type, against antigens, especially
cellular antigens, bacteria or parasites, present in the macrophage
granuloma and may be initiated by macrophage-activating products released from T-lymphocytes on contact with antigen (25, 27).

The injection of suspensions of bacteria such as B. pertussis into a
localized site gives rise to what has been termed a "high-turnover-
granuloma" (36, 37, 40), in which macrophages show a higher than normal
proportion of mitotic forms, enhanced DNA and protein synthesis and the
numbers of macrophages reaching and leaving the lesion at any time are
much greater than in control lesions induced with carrageenan. It is
difficult to "activate" macrophages in vitro. However, WYNNE et al.
(51) and ADOLPHE et al. (1) have recently shown that addition of inflammatory exudates to macrophage cultures in vitro provides the cells
with undefined factors which allow them to synthesize DNA and to divide.

Enhancement of cytotoxic activity in macrophages is not achieved rapidly. It requires differentiation of the cells from a less active precusor population and is associated with increased synthesis of DNA and protein, including lysosomal hydrolases (15). As mentioned above, this differentiation usually takes days or weeks. However, other macrophage activities are stimulated immediately on contact with appropriate factors. These include phagocytosis, the fusion of lysosomes with phagosomes, and extracellular release of hydrolases by exocytosis. They also include the enhancement of locomotion by chemical substances and the chemotactic orientation of locomotion. These activities do not require synthesis of new protein and they can be observed readily in vitro. They are associated with a rapid burst of metabolism in the cell, measured by consumption of glucose or oxygen and accumulation of lactate (24). These functions are activated as soon as blood monocytes respond to an inflammatory stimulus and enter a lesion. The newly arrived macrophages show activity for a short time and then may become quiescent. During this quiescent period they may be reconstituting plasma membrane lost by interiorization during phagocytosis (42). They also begin protein synthesis to replace hydrolases and other proteins. Eventually, if the initial stimulus continues, these macrophages regain activity and may perform more efficiently than previously.

It is perhaps best to avoid the word "activation" when speaking of the immediate, short-term events in macrophages. However, both short-term and long-term events occur in response to signals from outside the cell, i.e. they are membrane-mediated events. We are beginning to understand how short-term events in macrophages could be signalled, but are still quite ignorant about the long-term ones. It is possible that similar signals are recognized in both cases. I should like to discuss the possible mechanisms for membrane-mediated triggering of such events as chemotaxis and phagocytosis in macrophages and to speculate how these may be relevant to macrophage "activation" as discussed above.


CONTRACTILE PROTEINS AND CALCIUM


Phagocytosis, exocytosis, lysosome-phagosome fusion and chemotaxis are events which involve displacements either of portions of the cell or of the whole cell. It seems likely, but has not been conclusively proved, that these displacements are achieved by contraction and relaxation of microfilaments composed of actin and myosin which slide on each other as in muscle and which exist in the cell cytoplasm in an equilibrium between assembly and disassembly (22, 23). Both microfilaments and microtubules have been observed in macrophages (5, 8, 9, 34). Microtubules appear to form a rigid cytoskeleton within the cell which imparts directionality to the microfilament-mediated fine movements. Thus if microtubule assembly is blocked with colchicine or vinblastine or similar drugs, the oriented movement necessary for chemotaxis is lost. The macrophages migrate as rapidly as untreated cells but their migration is now random, not directional (4, 5, 7). This type of observation can be confirmed in Boyden-chamber experiments in which the concentration of the attractant is varied above and below the filter (author's unpublished observations). Similarly, in colchicine-treated cells, phagocytosis is not blocked but the ordered movement of endocytosed vesicles to the Golgi region is lost and the vesicles move in the cytoplasm in a less directional manner (9).

Cytoplasmic contractile proteins resemble those of muscle and, like them, are probably functionally regulated by the intracellular divalent cation concentration. Normally the cytoplasmic $Ca^{2+}$ concentration is too low for contraction of microfilaments ($<10^{-7}M$). Appropriate membrane-mediated signals allow an influx of $Ca^{2+}$ into the cytoplasm, either from outside or from intracellular storage vesicles whose nature is still unknown, and contraction then takes place ($10^{-5} - 10^{-6}M$) $Ca^{2+}$). Since the $Ca^{2+}$ concentration is normally lower in the cytoplasm than on the extracytoplasmic side of the membrane, active cation transport into the cytoplasm is not required. All that is needed is a transient increase of permeability of the membrane to $Ca^{2+}$ and a $Ca^{2+}$ gradient into the cell will be created. However for relaxation to occur, the $Ca^{2+}$ has to be pumped out of the cytoplasm and it is presumed that a membrane-bound $Ca^{2+}$-activated ATPase (39) operates this pump. I have recently observed (45) that the migration of blood monocytes is diminished but not totally abolished in $Ca^{2+}$- and $Mg^{2+}$-free media. If low concentrations ($10^{-9}M$) of the calcium ionophore A23187 (Eli-Lilly) are added to the cells, these cells migrate as well in $Ca^{2+}$, $Mg^{2+}$-free medium as in $Ca^{2+}$, $Mg^{2+}$-rich medium (45). This independence from extracellular cation concentration suggests that during locomotion the ionophore helps the cell to use its own stored intracellular divalent cations and strengthens the hypothesis that such stores must exist and be used in cell movement. This is also suggested by the work of WOODIN (50) who analysed the action of staphylococcal leucocidin in terms of ion movements across neutrophil membranes. Hydrolysis of ATP is required as an energy source for contraction and is achieved by the ATPase action of myosin. This energy (in the form of ATP) seems to be supplied chiefly from anaerobic glycolysis since inhibitors of anaerobic glycolysis, but not inhibitors of oxidative processes, block phagocytosis and chemotaxis (12, 13, 24, 38, 49). It is also possible that intracellular levels of cyclic nucleotides (cATMP, cGMP) regulate the function of cytoplasmic contractile systems in phagocytic cells (52, 53).


MEMBRANE SIGNALS FOR MACROPHAGE FUNCTIONS


I have suggested that chemotaxis of leucocytes, including macrophages, is triggered by substances which show an affinity for the hydrophobic interior of a cell-membrane bilayer such that they are able to penetrate into the bilayer and possibly to enhance its permeability to ions. The evidence for this suggestion was based on the finding that proteins could be made chemotactic by linking non-polar side-groups but not polar side-groups to them (45, 48) or by forms of denaturation which increased the hydrophobicity of the protein (44, 47). More recently we have found that lipids may enhance leucocyte locomotion and that this enhancement, although often weak, is stronger for macrophages and monocytes than for neutrophils. A lipid with chemoattractant properties for mononuclear phagocytes has been isolated from Corynebacterium parvum and related organisms (35). This lipid may initiate locomotion by an interaction with lipids in macrophage membranes but presumably has a lower affinity for neutrophil membranes. This suggests that the interaction sites in the two cell types are not identical. Furthermore, there is evidence that hydrophobic interactions between phagocyte and particle are important for phagocytosis (29, 30, 31, 32, 41) and that hydrophilic particles (e.g. capsulated bacteria) resist phagocytosis because they are unable to form hydrophobic interactions with phagocyte membranes.

Clustering of membrane proteins may lead to formation of membrane "pores" allowing ingress of cations and it is therefore possible that

macrophage functions could be triggered following protein clustering
Among the interesting possibilities, one is that opsonizing antibodies
bound to particles may link by their Fc fragments to the macrophage
membrane and form clusters which initiate phagocytosis of the opsonized
particle. In the same way, cytophilic antibody bound to macrophages
by its Fc fragment may, on binding to polyvalent antigen, become cross-
linked to form clusters. It seems possible that following antigen binding by Fab, a conformational change (21) is induced in the cell-bound
Fc fragment. Such a change in Fc may increase its hydrophobicity and allow it to penetrate into the lipid bilayer thus initiating the necessary
increase in membrane permeability. JENSEN and ESQUENAZI (23) have shown
that cytophilic antibody on neutrophils, on binding to antigen, induces
the neutrophil to migrate in a gradient of that antigen but not of
other antigens. We have shown in work with VASQUEZ (unpublished results)
that a similar antigen-dependent chemotaxis occurs in guinea-pig peritoneal macrophages coated with the cytophilic antibody. These findings
support the idea that phagocyte functions are activated by the Fc fragment of membrane-bound IgG on contact with antigen.

The above description of macrophage stimulation is still largely hypothetical, but appears plausible at the present time. One major problem
is how, if cytoplasmic motility is controlled by release of cations
from intracellular reserves, this intracellular event can be controlled
directly by factors acting on the external side of the plasma membrane.
The sarcoplasmic reticulum, the calcium store of muscle, is in contact
with tubules which run into the cell from the plasma membrane and which
depolarize when it depolarizes. Thus the signal is transmitted directly
to the sarcoplasmic reticulum. It is not known whether analogous structures exist in non-muscle cells.


## THE CELL MEMBRANE AND LONG-TERM MACROPHAGE ACTIVATION


There is no direct evidence to suggest that the delayed events which
are necessary for the differentiation of macrophages into cytotoxic
forms are controlled by membrane-mediated signals of the type described
above. However evidence is beginning to appear that influxes of divalent
cations into the cytoplasm play an important role in cell differentiation, although these experiments have not been done in macrophages.
Fibroblast differentiation may be influenced in this way (16, 20).
Mitogen-induced lymphocyte transformation is dependent on the presence
of extracellular $Ca^{2+}$ (3, 6, 17, 43) and mitogens induce $Ca^{2+}$ influxes
in lymphocytes (19). These influxes are enhanced by dibutyryl cGMP
and inhibited by dibutyryl cAMP. MAINO et al. (26) reported that mitosis of lymphocytes can be induced by the presence of the ionophore
A23187. The cells required to be incubated with A23187 for 48 h whereas
the effects described earlier of this ionophore on cell locomotion are
immediate. However, FREEDMAN et al. (19) reported that B-cell mitogens
did not cause $Ca^{2+}$ uptake by B cells, so presumably $Ca^{2+}$ is not a prerequisite for all forms of differentiation. It would be interesting
to apply this sort of approach to macrophage differentiation.

One of the obvious differences between the effects of mitogens or ionophores on cell differentiation as described above and their effects on
contractile events such as chemotaxis or phagocytosis is that for the
latter events only a brief period of stimulation (minutes) is required
to induce the cell to move or to ingest material, whereas if cells
are to be induced to go into mitosis or to synthesize DNA it appears
to be essential that they remain in contact with the stimulant over a
long time interval (days). For instance, PHA-induced DNA synthesis

by lymphocytes can be prevented by removing calcium from the medium at any time up to 36 h after addition to the mitogen (17, 43). This necessity for prolonged contact may prove to be important for macrophage activation. This is suggested by comparing the prolonged effects in vivo of injection of casein, on the one hand, and C. parvum or other anaerobic coryneforms on the other. Both have short-term stimulating effects on macrophages. Both casein and C. parvum are chemotactic for macrophages and both induce a macrophage exudate 2-5 days after injection into the peritoneal cavity of the guinea-pig (49). However after casein-induction, these macrophages disappear from the peritoneal cavity soon afterwards. Casein is highly susceptible to hydrolysis by proteases and is probably quickly removed from the inflammatory site. Once it is removed, no further stimulus to the macrophages remains. On the other hand, after induction with anaerobic coryneforms - and still more so with M. tuberculosis - a macrophage exudate persists and, after 21 days, a population of macrophages is present which is synthesizing protein, has quite a lot of rough endoplasmic reticulum and much higher levels of lysosomal hydrolases than the original population which was present at three days (14). It may be that particulate membrane stimulants and especially indigestible bacteria such as M. tuberculosis, which may survive undigested for weeks inside a macrophage, provide the right kind of persistent membrane pertubation to induce the delayed events involved in macrophage activation. The extracted and purified chemoattractant lipid from C. parvum (35) - which may be similar to the lipid described by FAUVE and HEVIN (18) with macrophage-stimulating amd anti-tumour effects in vivo - acts more weakly as a long-term macrophage stimulant in vivo than the whole organism from which it was derived. However, if the purified lipid is linked to Sephadex beads, it recovers some macrophage-stimulating activity, possibly because it can now be cleared only slowly from the injection site (experiments of R.J.RUSSELL and K.FRYER).

Although we do not understand how external stimuli induce macrophages to differentiate and to become activated, it seems likely that the stimulus must remain in contact with the cell for a prolonged interval, probably days. Obviously soluble materials may be ineffective because they diffuse away or are digested. Indigestible particles and especially bacteria which persist in the lesion are better candidates as macrophage activators, particularly if they are antigenic and induce a T-lymphocyte response. It would be interesting if some of the unique properties of mycobacterial adjuvants could be explained in terms of their affinities for cell membranes.


## SUMMARY

A number of short-term macrophage functions are stimulated immediately on contact of suitable external materials with the macrophage plasma membrane. These include locomotion and chemotaxis, phagocytosis, and exocytosis of lysosomal hydrolases. They are probably contractile events and may be initiated by a transient increase in permeability to divalent cations either of the plasma membrane or of hypothetical intracellular cations stores. Such permeability changes may follow interaction of hydrophobic substances with the membrane bilayer or follow contact with substances which induce clustering of membrane proteins. It is conjectured that similar substances might induce long-term events such as DNA and protein synthesis, mitosis and activation of cytotoxic function in macrophages, but that to do this, contact of the substance with the macrophage must be prolonged.

The work of the author described here was supported by the Medical Research Council.

## REFERENCES

1. Adolphe, M., Fontagne, J., Pelletier, M., Giroud, J.P.: Induction of DNA synthesis in rat macrophages in vitro by inflammatory exudate. Nature 253, 637 (1975)
2. Alexander, P., Evans, R.: Endotoxin and double stranded RNA render macrophage cytotoxic. Nature (New Biol.) 232, 76 (1971)
3. Alford, R.H.: Metal cation requirements for phytohaemagglutinin-induced transformation of human peripheral blood lymphocytes. J. Immunol. 104, 698 (1970)
4. Allison, A.C.: Mechanism of movement and maintenance of polarity in leucocytes. Antibodies and chemotherapy 19, 191 (1974)
5. Allison, A.C., Davies, P., De Petris, S.: Role of contractile microfilaments in macrophage movement and endocytosis. Nature (New Biol.) 232, 153 (1971)
6. Allwood, G., Asherson, G.L., Davey, M.J., Goodford, P.J.: The early uptake of radioactive calcium by human lymphocytes treated with phytohaemagglutinin. Immunol. 21, 509 (1971)
7. Bandmann, V., Rydgren, L., Norberg, B.: The difference between random movement and chemotaxis. Exp. Cell. Res. 88, 63 (1974)
8. Bhisey, A.N., Freed, J.J.: Ameboid movement induced in cultured macrophages by colchicine and vinblastine. Exp. Cell. Res. 64, 419 (1971)
9. Bhisey, A.N., Freed, J.J.: Altered movement of endosomes in colchicine-treated cultured macrophages. Exp. Cell. Res. 64, 430 (1971)
10. Blanden, R.V.: Modification of macrophage function. J. reticulo-endothel. Soc. 5, 179 (1968)
11. Blanden, R.V.: Increased antibacterial resistance and immunodepression during graft-versus-host reactions in mice. Transplantation 7, 484 (1969)
12. Carruthers, B.M.: Leukocyte motility I. Method of study, normal variation, effect of physical alterations in environment and effect of iodoacetate. Can. J. Physiol. Pharmacol. 44, 475 (1966)
13. Carruthers, B.M.: Leukocyte motility II. Effect of absence of glucose in medium: effect of presence of deoxyglucose, dinitrophenyl, puromycin, actinomycin D and trypsin on the response to chemotactic substance: effect of segregation of cells from chemotactic substance. Can. J. Physiol. Pharmacol. 45, 269 (1967)
14. Cater, J.C.: Ph. D. thesis., University of Glasgow, 1974

15. Cohn, Z.A.: The structure and function of monocytes and macrophages. Adv. Immunol. 9, 163 (1968)
16. Dulbecco, R., Elkington, J.: Induction of growth in resting fibroblastic cell culture by $Ca^{2+}$. Proc. Nat. Acad. Sci. U.S. 72, 1584 (1975)
17. Diamantstein, T., Ulmer, A.: The control of immune response in vitro by $Ca^{2+}$. II. The $Ca^{2+}$ dependent period during mitogenic stimulation. Immunol. 28, 121 (1975)
18. Fauve, R.M., Hevin, B.: Immunostimulation with bacterial phospholipid extracts. Proc. Nat. Acad. Sci. U.S. 71, 573 (1974)
19. Freedman, M.H., Raff, M.C., Gomperts, B.: Induction of increased calcium uptake in mouse T lymphocytes by concanavalin A and its modulation by cyclic nucleotides. Nature 255, 378 (1975)
20. Gail, M.H., Boone, C.W., Thompson, C.S.: A calcium requirement for fibroblast motility and proliferation. Exp. Cell. Res. 79, 386 (1973)

21. Givol, D., Pecht, I., Hochman, J., Schlessinger, J., Steinberg, I. Z.: Conformational changes in the Fab and Fc of the antibody as a consequence of antigen binding. In: Progress in Immunology II. Brent, L. and Holborow, E.J. (eds.). Amsterdam: North-Holland, 1974, Vol. I, p. 39

22. Huxley, H.E.: Muscular contraction and cell motility. Nature 243, 445 (1973)

23. Jensen, J.A., Esquenazi, V.: Chemotactic stimulation by cell surface immune reactions. Nature 256, 213 (1975)

24. Karnovsky, M.L., Simmons, S., Glass, E.A., Shafer, A.W., D'Arcy Hart, P.: Metabolism of macrophages. In: Mononuclear phagocytes. Van Furth, R. (ed.). Oxford: Blackwell, 1970, p. 103

25. Mackaness, G.B.: Cellular Immunity. In: Mononuclear phagocytes. Van Furth, R. (ed.). Oxford: Blackwell, 1970, p. 461

26. Maino, V.C., Green, N.M., Crumpton, M.J.: The role of calcium ions in initiating transformation of lymphocytes. Nature 251, 324 (1974)

27. Mauel, J.: Cell-mediated immune mechanisms in bacterial and protozoal infections. In: Progress in Immunology II. Brent, L., Holborow, E.J. (eds.). Amsterdam: North-Holland, 1974, Vol. IV, p. 109

28. North, R.J.: Cellular kinetics associated with the development of acquired cellular resistance. J. exp. Med. 130, 299 (1969)

29. Van Oss, C.J., Gillman, C.F.: Phagocytosis as a surface phenomenon I. Contact angles and phagocytosis of non-opsonized bacteria. J. reticuloendothel. Soc. 12, 283 (1972)

30. Van Oss, C.J., Gillman, C.F.: Phagocytosis as a surface phenomenon II. Contact angles and phagocytosis of encapsulated bacteria before and after opsonization by specific antibody and complement. J. reticuloendothel. Soc. 12, 497 (1972)

31. Van Oss, C.J., Gillman, C.F.: Phagocytosis as a surface phenomenon III. Influence of C1423 on the contact angle and on the phagocytosis of sensitized encapsulated bacteria. Immunol. Commun. 2, 415 (1973)

32. Van Oss, C.J., Gillman, C.F., Neumann, A.W.: Phagocytosis as a surface phenomenon IV. The minimum size and composition of antigen-antibody complexes that can become phagocytized. Immunol Commun. 3, 77 (974)

33. Pollard, T.D., Weihing, R.A.: Actin and myosin and cell movement CRC Crit. Rev. Biochem. 2, 1 (1972)

34. Reaven, E.P., Axline, S.G.: Subplasmalemmal microfilaments and microtubules in resting and phagocytizing cultivated macrophages. J. Cell. Biol. 59, 12 (1973)

35. Russell, R.J., Mc Inroy, R.J., Wilkinson, P.C., White, R.G.: A lipid chemotactic factor from anaerobic coryneform bacteria including Corynebacterium parvum with activity for macrophages and monocytes. Immunol. 30, 935 (1976)

36. Ryan, G.B., Spector, W.G.: Natural selection of long lived macrophages in experimental granulomata. J. Pathol. 99, 139 (1969)

37. Ryan, G.B., Spector, W.G.: Macrophage turnover in inflamed connective tissue. Proc. Roy. Soc. B. 175, 269 (1970)

38. Sbarra, A.J., Karnovsky, M.L.: The biochemical basis of phagocytosis I. Metabolic changes during the ingestion of particles by polymorphonuclear phagocytes. J. Biol. Chem. 234, 1355 (1959)

39. Schatzmann, H.J.: Active calcium transport and $Ca^{2+}$ activated ATPase in human red cells. Current Topics in Membranes and Transport 6, 125 (1975)

40. Spector, W.G., Ryan, G.B.: The mononuclear phagocyte in inflammation. In: "Mononuclear phagocytes". Van Furth R. (ed.). Oxford: Blackwell, 1970, p. 219

41. Thrasher, S.G., Yoshida, T., Van Oss, C.J., Cohen, S., Rose, N.R.: Alteration of macrophage interfacial tension by supernatants of antigen-activated lymphocyte cultures. J. Immunol. 110, 321 (1973)

47

42. Werb, Z., Cohn, Z.A.: Plasma membrane synthesis in the macrophage following phagocytosis of polystyrene latex particles. J. Biol. Chem. 247, 2439 (1972)
43. Whitney, R.B., Sutherland, R.M.: Requirement for calcium ions in lymphocyte transformation by phytohemagglutinin. J. Cell. Physiol. 80, 329 (1972)
44. Wilkinson, P.C.: Surface and cell membrane activities of leukocyte chemotactic factors. Nature 251, 58 (1974)
45. Wilkinson, P.C.: Leukocyte locomotion and chemotaxis. The influence of divalent cations and cation ionophores. Exp. Cell. Res. 93, 420 (1975)
46. Wilkinson, P.C.: Cellular and molecular aspects of chemotaxis of macrophages and monocytes. In: Immunobiology of the macrophage. Nelson D.S. (ed.). New York: Academic Press, 1976, p. 349
47. Wilkinson, P.C., Mc Kay, I.C.: The chemotactic activity of native and denatured serum albumin. Int. Archs. Allergy Appl. Immunol. 41, 237 (1971)
48. Wilkinson, P.C., Mc Kay, I.C.: The molecular requirements for chemotactic attraction of leukocytes by proteins. Studies of proteins with synthetic side groups. Europ. J. Immunol. 2, 570 (1972)
49. Wilkinson, P.C., O'Neill, G.J., Mc Inroy, R.J., Cater, J.C., Roberts, J.A.: Chemotaxis of macrophages: The role of a macrophage specific cytotaxin from anaerobic corynebacteria and its relation to immunopotentiation in vivo. In: Immunopotentiation. Ciba Foundation Symposium, 18. Amsterdam. Associated Scientific Publishers, pp. 121-135, 1973
50. Woodin, A.M.: Staphylococcal leukocidin. In: The Staphylococci, Cohen J.O. (ed.). New York: Wiley, 1972, pp. 281-299
51 Wynne, K.M., Spector, W.G., Willoughby, D.A.: Macrophage proliferation in vitro induced by exudates. Nature 253, 636 (1975)
52. Zurier, R.B., Hoffstein, S., Weissmann, G.: Mechanisms of lysosomal enzyme release from human leukocytes. I. Effect of cyclic nucleotides and colchicine. J. Cell. Biol. 58, 27 (1973)
53. Zurier, R.B., Weissmann, G., Hoffstein, S., Kammerman, S., Tai, H. H.: Mechanisms of lysosomal enzyme release from human leukocytes II. Effects of cAMP and cGMP autonomic agonists and agents which affect microtubule function. J. Clin. Invest. 53, 297 (1974)

# Chapter 7
# Lymphocyte-Macrophage Interactions in BCG-Treated Mice

I. FLORENTIN, M. BRULEY-ROSSET, and M. DAVIGNY

## INTRODUCTION

A previous study to investigate the mode of action of BCG showed that in mice, adjuvant modulated some immune responses via an action on macrophages (4). Indeed, splenic macrophages were responsible for the unresponsiveness of the T-lymphocytes to mitogens in vitro observed after BCG injection, whereas such a response was unaffected in B-lymphocytes. In addition, peritoneal macrophages were activated as shown by their capacity to kill non-specifically tumor cells in vitro. These findings showed that BCG could simultaneously exert stimulating and inhibitory effects through macrophage and lymphocyte interactions. These results were observed after injection of 1 mg of BCG. The question arises whether increasing doses of adjuvant could modify the level of macrophage activation, the production of inhibitory macrophages, and perhaps extend their suppressive activity to both T- and B-lymphocytes. Indeed, injection of high doses of BCG were shown to depress the antibody response to sheep red blood cells (6) and to inhibit the capacity of T-lymphocytes to elicit a graft-versus-host reaction (5). Perhaps all schedules that induce immune stimulation by BCG may have the adverse side effect of inhibiting lymphocyte functions. In the present work, BCG was administered i.v. at various doses, 14 days before testing macrophage activation and spleen-cell responsiveness to T- and B-cell mitogens in vitro. This route and time of administration were chosen since they were clearly shown to be optimal in previous studies (2, 10). This study could contribute to clarify the optimal conditions of BCG administration for which stimulatory effects would have the better of inhibitory effects.

## MATERIAL AND METHODS

### Mice

Three-month-old DBA/2, C57Bl/6, and (DBA/2xC57Bl/6)Fl mice (Centre d'élevage d'Orléans, La Source) were used.

### Tumor

L1210 (DBA/2) and EAkR (C57Bl/6) leukemias were maintained in ascitic form by weekly intraperitoneal (i.p.) passage into mice of the original strain.

## Bacillus Calmette-Guérin (BCG)

A fresh preparation of living BCG (Pasteur Institute) was injected i.v. at the dose of 1, 3, and 5 mg per mouse (7 x $10^6$ viable units/mg) 14 days before the tests.

## Macrophage Cytotoxic Assay

The technique has been previously described in detail ($\underline{4}$). Briefly, macrophages were harvested from the peritoneum of normal or BCG-treated mice and cultivated as monolayers. $^{51}$Cr-labeled tumor cells (L1210 or EAkR leukemic cells) were added to the macrophage monolayer at the optimal ratio of one target cell to twenty macrophages ($10^5$ tumor cells to 2 x $10^6$ macrophages in 1 ml). After incubation at 37°C for 18 h the amount of $^{51}$Cr released from tumor cells was determined.

Results are expressed as the arithmetic mean of counts per minute (cpm) in 12 macrophage cultures ± standard error of the mean (S.E.M).

## Cell Fractionation

Spleen-cell suspensions were prepared from normal and BCG-treated mice and fractionated by two techniques which have been previously described in detail ($\underline{4}$).

Spleen cells were passed through nylon-wool colums according to the technique of JULIUS et al. ($\underline{7}$). The recovered nylon nonadherent population is known to be considerably enriched in T cells by depletion in B cells and macrophages.

To obtain macrophage-depleted populations, spleen-cell suspensions were treated by carbonyl iron and magnet and allowed to adhere to plastic.

## Mitogen Responses

The responses of unfractionated and purified spleen cells to nonspecific mitogens were tested as previously described ($\underline{4}$).

Briefly, 5 x $10^5$ spleen cells in 0.2 ml of RPMI 1640 culture medium supplemented with 10% mule serum (Gibco) and antibiotics, were plated into culture microplates (Microtest II, Falcon) and 20 µl of phyto-hemagglutinin-P (PHA) (Wellcome Laboratories), diluted 1:50; or lipopolysaccharide from Escherischia Coli (LPS) (Difco) at 100 µg per ml; or concanavalin A (Con A) at 250 µg/ml (Pharmacia Fine Chemicals); were added.

The cultures were incubated for 48 h at 37°C and then pulsed with 1 µCi $^3$H-thymidine (specific activity: 20 Ci/m mole) (CEA, France), harvested 6 h later and processed for radioactivity counting.

Results are expressed as meian cpm of triplicate cultures ± S.E.M..

RESULTS

## Effect of the Dose of BCG on Macrophage Cytotoxic Activity

Results presented in Table 1 show that, as reported previously (4), 1 mg
BCG given i.v. strongly enhanced the cytotoxic potential of peritoneal
macrophages for tumor cells in vitro. A 64% increase in $^{51}$Cr release
was observed when the labeled tumor cells were exposed to BCG-treated
macrophages, compared to the exposure to normal macrophage monolayers.
Macrophages from mice given 3 or 5 mg of BCG also displayed a high
cytotoxic activity (50% increase of $^{51}$Cr release from the target cells),
which is weakly but not significantly different from the one exerted
by macrophages treated with 1 mg BCG. The percentage of $^{51}$Cr released
from tumor cells exposed to monolayers of normal macrophages was 30-
40% of the total radioactivity added to each culture. The results were
similar when EAkR were used instead of L1210 tumor cells.

Table 1. In vitro cytotoxic activity against L1210 tumor cells of
peritoneal macrophages from mice injected with various doses of BCG

| Dose of BCG (mg) | Mean (cpm)$^a$ ± S.E. S.E. | P values$^b$ | Mean spleen weight (mg) |
| --- | --- | --- | --- |
| 1 | 2,119 ± 78 | P < 0.001 | 230 |
| 3 | 1,951 ± 55 | P < 0.001 | 434 |
| 5 | 1,945 ± 62 | P < 0.001 | 632 |
| Controls | 1,296 ± 42 | | 90 |

$^a$ $^{51}$Cr release (in cpm) from labeled tumor cells exposed to monolayers
of macrophages from normal mice (controls) or BCG-treated mice. Mean
number of cpm ± S.E. in 12 macrophage cultures.
$^b$ P values were determined by the Student's-t-test.

## Effect of the Dose of BCG on the Mitogen Responsiveness of Spleen Cells

Spleen cells from normal mice and from BCG-treated mice were compared
for their ability to respond in vitro to T-cell mitogens, PHA and Con
A, and to a B-cell mitogen, LPS. The results of a typical experiment
are presented in Table 2.

Unfractionated spleen cells from BCG-treated mice incorporated about
three times more $^3$H-thymidine than normal spleen cells. They were markedly refractory to stimulation by PHA and Con A and a dose-effect
relationship was observed. An 85% and 75% depression of $^3$H-TdR uptake
was observed in spleen cells treated with 1 mg BCG when stimulated by
PHA and Con A respectively as compared to normal spleen cells. This
depressive effect reached a plateau of 90-94% with spleen cells taken
from mice given either 3 mg or 5 mg of BCG. In contrast, the response
to LPS was unaffected after 1 mg of BCG and was significantly enhanced
after 3 mg (40% increase of LPS induced $^3$H-thymidine uptake) and 5 mg
(74% increase) compared to normal spleen cells.

Removal of macrophages from spleen-cell suspensions treated with 1 mg
BCG resulted in a complete restoration of their PHA and Con A responsiveness. The degree of restoration induced by this treatment then
decreased as a function of the dose of BCG injected and of the T-cell

Table 2. Effect of BCG injected at various doses on the mitogen responsiveness of unfractionated spleen cells and macrophage-depleted spleen cells

| Source of cells | Mitogen added to the cultures | Dose of BCG | | | |
|---|---|---|---|---|---|
| | | None (Controls) | 1 mg | 3 mg | 5 mg |
| Unfractionated spleen cells | None | 936 ± 76(a) | 2,352 ± 84 | 2,943 ± 95 | 2,700 ± 170 |
| | PHA | 52,662 ± 4,717 | 7,777 ± 238 | 4,968 ± 234 | 3,513 ± 60 |
| | Con A | 40,344 ± 6,388 | 9,982 ± 143 | 3,237 ± 225 | 2,508 ± 125 |
| | LPS | 25,756 ± 1,874 | 25,932 ± 1,731 | 35,711 ± 2,577 | 43,502 ± 6,393 |
| Macrophage-depleted spleen cells | None | 914 ± 190 | 2,215 ± 102 | 2,711 ± 168 | 2,643 ± 90 |
| | PHA | 41,787 ± 6,635 | 43,653 ± 6,810 | 17,627 ± 1,722 | 7,813 ± 848 |
| | Con A | 55,442 ± 7,219 | 52,177 ± 4,709 | 42,987 ± 2,072 | 30,470 ± 902 |
| | LPS | 24,194 ± 971 | 32,749 ± 4,706 | 37,573 ± 3,326 | 24,562 ± 777 |
| Spleen weight (mg) | | 114 | 181 | 340 | 706 |

a Mean cpm ± S.E. Cultures were done in triplicate.

mitogen used for the stimulation. Indeed, the PHA response was reduced by 58% and 81% in spleen cells treated with 3 and 5 mg BCG respectively, compared to macrophage-depleted normal spleen cells, whereas only a 22% and 45% reduction of the Con A response was simultaneously observed. The LPS response was not significantly modified by macrophage depletion in normal and BCG-treated spleen cells, except for cells treated with 5 mg BCG, the response of which was significantly depressed when compared to unfractionated spleen cells.

The above experiments demonstrated that macrophages alone were not responsible for the defective T-mitogen responsiveness of spleen cells given high doses of BCG. To further clarify this point, we tested whether T-lymphocytes could not also exert an inhibitory effect. Spleen cells were purified by passage through nylon-wool columns and the PHA response of the nylon-nonadherent population, considerably enriched in T-lymphocytes, was compared to that of unfractionated and of macrophage-depleted spleen cells.

Results presented in Table 3 show that unseparated spleen cells were again completely refractory to PHA stimulation whatever the dose, 1 or 3 mg, of BCG injected. Macrophage depletion led to a nearly complete restoration of the PHA responsiveness of spleen cells treated with 1 mg BCG, whereas a 58% reduction was still observed in spleen cells treated with 3 mg BCG, compared to macrophage-depleted normal spleen cells.

The defective PHA response of BCG-treated spleen cells could be restored by passage of the cells through nylon-wool columns but the degree of restoration depended upon the dose of BCG injected. Only a 30% reduction of the mitogen-induced $^3$H-thymidine uptake was observed in nylon-nonadherent spleen cells treated with 1 mg BCG, whereas the response was reduced by 57% in spleen cells treated with 3 mg BCG, when compared to nylon-passaged normal spleen cells.


DISCUSSION


The results presented here demonstrate that BCG, injected i.v. into mice at various doses, markedly affects macrophages which are activated and are instrumental in the depression of spleen cell responsiveness to T-cell mitogens consistently observed after BCG. They also provide evidence that this T-cell defect both results from macrophage-lymphocyte and lymphocyte-lymphocyte interactions as long as high doses of BCG are concerned.

Whilst investigating the effect of increasing doses of BCG upon macrophage activation, we observed that the cytotoxic activity of peritoneal macrophages against tumor cells in vitro reached a maximal level after 1 mg of BCG and remained as a plateau after 3 or 5 mg of BCG. It is possible that 1 mg of BCG induced maximal activation of macrophages. In previous studies it was shown that in vivo macrophage activation by BCG well manifested itself in the presence of T-cells (2) but that a direct action of BCG on macrophages may also be involved (3). It was also demonstrated that BCG-activated macrophages inhibited some T-lymphocyte functions (4, 5). All these data could suggest that some equilibrium is established between macrophage activation by T-lymphocytes or directly by BCG on one hand, and T-lymphocyte suppression by activated macrophages, on the other hand, and is responsible for the constant level of the macrophage cytotoxic potential whatever the dose of BCG injected.

Table 3. Effects of the removal of nylon-adherent cells and of plastic-adherent phagocytic cells on the mitogen responsiveness of spleen cells from BCG-treated mice

| Source of cells | Mitogen added to the cultures | Dose of BCG | | |
| --- | --- | --- | --- | --- |
| | | None (Controls) | 1 mg | 3 mg |
| Unfractionated spleen cells | None | 1,560 ± 210[a] | 1,716 ± 67 | 1,631 ± 34 |
| | PHA | 41,882 ± 4,658 | 2,217 ± 184 | 1,885 ± 115 |
| | LPS | 18,560 ± 881 | 28,546 ± 5,600 | 37,365 ± 4,110 |
| Nylon non-adherent spleen cells | None | 826 ± 28 | 2,236 ± 115 | 3,173 ± 156 |
| | PHA | 33,123 ± 1,582 | 23,112 ± 1,108 | 17,402 ± 2,660 |
| Macrophage-depleted spleen cells | None | 1,339 ± 243 | 2,510 ± 98 | 5,150 ± 203 |
| | PHA | 25,718 ± 2,588 | 21,112 ± 3,590 | 11,292 ± 2,363 |
| | LPS | 28,734 ± 1,113 | 37,493 ± 3,628 | 28,676 ± 1,594 |
| Spleen weight (mg)[b] | | 110 ± 5 | 460 ± 32 | 780 ± 52 |

[a] Mean cpm ± S.E. Cultures were done in triplicate.
[b] Mean spleen weight ± S.E Groups of 4 animals.

We have already shown that spleen cells from mice treated with 1 mg BCG were nearly totally unresponsive to Con A, whereas they had an improved response to dextran sulfate, a B-cell mitogen (4). The present study demonstrates that the response to PHA was depressed as markedly as that to Con A and that both responses were nearly completely inhibited after 1 mg of BCG. In contrast, a direct relationship between the degree of enhancement of the response to a B-cell mitogen, LPS, and the dose of BCG was observed.

The impairment of the activity of T cells to divide in response to Con A in spleen cells treated with 1 mg BCG was shown to be due to the inhibitory action of macrophages since macrophage-depleted spleen cells exhibited a normal response and BCG-treated macrophages completely inhibited the Con A response of normal spleen cells (4). The present study shows that the efficiency of macrophage removal in restoring PHA and Con A responsiveness of BCG-treated spleen cells decreased when the dose of BCG was increased. Moreover, this treatment more easily restored spleen-cell responsiveness to Con A than to PHA, whatever the dose of BCG. These data strongly suggest that a mechanism other than the inhibitory action of macrophages may also contribute to the T-cell defect observed after injection of high doses of BCG. There are at least three explanations for these findings: (a) mitogen-reactive T cells are diluted out by unreactive cells which are not removed by the carbonyl iron and magnet technique and adherency to plastic and which proliferate only after injection of high doses of BCG; (b) high doses of BCG induce suppressor cells which are not removed by the same technique; (c) high doses of BCG directly "paralyze" mitogen-reactive T cells. T-cell enriched populations from spleen cells treated with 3 and 5 mg BCG prepared by nylon-wool passage and as such depleted of both B cells and macrophages, exhibited the same degree of unresponsiveness to PHA or Con A as the respective macrophage-depleted spleen cells. This finding excluded the possibility than mitogen-reactive cells were diluted out by B cells. Recent experiments which are not reported here have demonstrated that these T-cell enriched suspensions inhibit the response of normal spleen cells and so strongly support the second hypothesis that high doses of BCG induce suppressor cells having characteristics of T cells. These observations are in agreement with those of GEFFARD and ORBACH (5) who reported the induction of suppressor T cells by injection of 3 mg of BCG, which inhibit the graft-versus-host reactivity in vivo and the helper activity in vitro of normal T-lymphocytes. Both types of suppressor cells appeared to be ineffective in decreasing B-cell activity since LPS responses were not depressed even after high doses of BCG.

Nevertheless it appears from these investigations that the main effect of BCG is exerted through macrophages, irrespective of the dose injected. Experiments are presently in progress to etablish whether the activated macrophage and the suppressor macrophage are identical. Adjuvant-activated macrophages exerting inhibitory activity on T-lymphocytes stimulated by mitogens in vitro have been described by SCOTT (12, 13) and by KIRCHNER et al. (8) after injection of Corynebacterium parvum. The latter authors, moreover, observed that after injection of high doses of the adjuvant, both T- and B-cell mitogen responses were equally suppressed by activated macrophages. Another discrepancy between C. parvum and BCG effects resides in the fact that macrophages activated by C. parvum seem to be instrumental in depressing cell-mediated immunity in vivo (14). Improvement of cell-mediated as well as humoral immune responses are generally reported after injection of moderate doses of BCG (1, 4, 9, 10, 11) suggesting that in these conditions suppressor macrophages were ineffective in vivo. Nevertheless, such a mechanism of suppression mediated by macrophages and perhaps by T-lymphocytes may be responsible for the impairment of immune responses observed after injection of high doses of BCG (6).

## SUMMARY

Fresh living Bacillus Calmette-Guérin (BCG), injected i.v. into (C57Bl/6xDBA/2)F1 mice, activated peritoneal macrophages rendering them highly cytotoxic for tumor cells in vitro. This cytotoxic activity was already maximal 14 days after injection of 1 mg of BCG and remained stable when 3 or 5 mg of BCG were given.

At the same time spleen cells of the BCG-treated mice showed strongly depressed responses to the T-cell mitogens, PHA and Con A, irrespective of the dose of BCG injected. The inhibitory effect was shown to be mediated by suppressor cells which had characteristics of macrophages since they could be removed by carbonyl iron and magnet treatment and were adherent to plastic. In contrast to it was observed after injection of 1 mg of BCG, these suppressor cells alone did not account for the depression of T-cell responses induced by higher doses of BCG. Nylon-nonadherent cell populations obtained from spleen cells treated with 3 or 5 mg BCG partially retained the inhibitory activity suggesting that suppressor T cells were also induced after injection of high doses of BCG.

In contrast, the responses to the B-cell mitogen LPS of unfractionated and macrophage-depleted spleen cells were not affected or significantly enhanced depending on the dose of BCG injected.

## REFERENCES

1. Balner, H., Old, L.J., Clarke, D.A.: Accelerated rejection of male skin isograft by female C57Bl/6 mice injected with Bacillus Calmette-Guérin. Proc. Soc. Exp. Biol. Med. 109, 58 (1962)
2. Bruley-Rosset, M., Florentin, I., Mathé, G.: In vivo and in vitro macrophage activation by systemic adjuvants. Agents and Action 6, 251 (1976)
3. Bruley-Rosset, M., Florentin, I., Khalil, A.M., Mathé, G.: Non-specific macrophage activation by sytemic adjuvants. Evaluation by lysosomal enzyme and in vitro tumoricidal activity. Int. Arch. All. Appl. Immunol. (in press)
4. Florentin, I., Huchet, R., Bruley-Rosset, M., Halle-Pannenko, O., Mathé, G.: Studies on the mechanism of action of BCG. Cancer Immunol. Immunoth. 1, 33 (1976)
5. Geffard, M., Orbach, S.: Enhancement of T suppressor activity in mice by high doses of BCG. Cancer Immunol. Immunoth. 1, 39 (1976)
6. Halle-Pannenko, O.: Comparison of various preparation of BCG in the experimental screening of the EORTC-ICIG. Cancer Immunol. Immunoth. 1, 41 (1976)
7. Julius, M.H., Simpson, E., Hertzenberg, L.A.: A rapid method for the isolation of functional thymus derived murine lymphocytes. Europ. J. Immunol. 3, 645 (1973)
8. Kirchner, H., Holden, H.T., Herberman, R.B.: Splenic suppressor macrophages induced in mice by injection of Corynebacterium parvum. J. of Immunol 115, 1212 (1975)
9. Mackaness, C.B., Lagrange, P.M., Ishibashi, T.: The modifying effect of BCG on the immunological induction of T cells. J. Exp. Med. 139, 1540 (1974)
10. Mathé, G., Kamel, !, Dezfulian, M., Halle-Pannenko, O., Bourut, C.: An experimental screening for "systemic adjuvants of immunity" applicable in cancer immunotherapy. Cancer Res. 33, 1987 (1973)

11. Miller, T.E., Mackaness, G.B., Lagrange, P.M.: Immunopotentiation with BCG. II Modulation of the response to sheep red blood cells. J. Nat. Cancer Inst. 51, 1669 (1973)
12. Scott, M.T.: Biological effects of the adjuvant Corynebacterium parvum. I. Inhibition of PHA, mixed lymphocyte and GVH reactivity. Cell. Immunol. 5, 459 (1972)
13. Scott, M.T.: Biological effects of adjuvant Corynebacterium parvum. II. Evidence for macrophage T-cell interaction. Cell. Immunol. 5, 468 (1972)
14. Scott, M.T.: Depression of delayed type hypersensitivity by Corynebacterium parvum. Mandatory role of the spleen. Cell Immunol, 13, 251 (1974)

# Chapter 8

# Liposomes as Immunological Adjuvants

A. C. ALLISON and G. GREGORIADIS

Adjuvants can be defined as agents which non-specifically increase immune responses to specific antigens. Some adjuvants, such as alum or Freund's incomplete adjuvant (FICA, a water-in-oil emulsion), increase the formation of antibodies against protein antigens without the development of delayed hypersensitivity. These can be termed type A (antibody-promoting) adjuvants. Others, such as Freund's complete adjuvant (FCA, with killed mycobacteria added to the incomplete adjuvant), promote delayed hypersensitivity as well as increasing antibody formation against protein antigens. These can be termed type C (cellmediated immunity-promoting) adjuvants. Evidence has been summarized (1) that many adjuvants exert their effects initially on macrophages and then on helper T-lymphocytes; for these the term T-adjuvants has been proposed. However, some adjuvants, such as bacterial lipopolysaccharide, appear to be able to stimulate B-lymphocytes directly without the agency of T-lymphocytes; these can be termed B-adjuvants.

After administration of antigen in Freund's adjuvant or alum, mononuclear cells invade the injection site and form granulomas; since the mineral oil in Freund's adjuvant and the alum are not biodegradable, the granulomas are persistent. This is unacceptable in human subjects. Freund's complete adjuvant, even when administered in very small doses in humans, induces severe granulomas. We have therefore attempted to find an adjuvant system composed of biodegradable materials which does not provoke granulomatous reactions. Liposomes, concentric spheres consisting of lipid bilayers separated by aqueous compartments, appear to fulfill these requirements. They may also be useful as carriers of materials that increase the capacity of macrophages to kill or inhibit the multiplication of tumour cells. Other adjuvants, such as BCG and Corynebacterium parvum, increase non-specifically host responses to tumour cells. The mode of action of such adjuvants is complex. They can promote cellmediated immunity, and with it, presumably, the capacity of T-lymphocytes to react against tumour cells. The adjuvants can increase the formation of antibodies against tumour antigens, which under some circumstances - especially in the presence of K cells - can have anti-tumour effects. Adjuvants can also increase the tumorostatic and tumoricidal capacity of macrophages; and the inhibition of BCG effects on tumour immunity by silica, reported from the laboratories of BALDWIN and SALOMON, indicates that macrophages play a role in this phenomenon.

It is generally agreed that successful immunization against tumours in man is likely to require adjuvants, as in the animal models where antigens are relatively "weak". Hence there is a need not only for clarifying how adjuvants exert their effects but also for the development of adjuvant systems that can be used in human subjects.

## STRUCTURE AND COMPOSITION OF LIPOSOMES

Procedures for the preparation of liposomes have been published by
BANGHAM et al. (4) and by PAPAHADJOPOULOS and MILLER (7). Lipids (usually phospholipids and cholesterol) are dried onto the surface of a
flask. An electrolyte solution is added  and the lipids are allowed
to swell with gentle agitation at room temperature. Mechanical agitation facilitates fragmentation of the micelles formed, producing liposomes varying from about 5-50 μm diameter. These can be broken down
further by the use of ultrasonics, which can produce liposomes as
small as those containing only a single lipid-bilayer surrounding an
aqueous compartment (about 50 nm diameter). The composition of the
lipid can be varied at will, and with it the stability, surface charge
and other properties of liposomes. For practical purposes we used mixtures of phosphatidylcholine (egg lecithin), cholesterol and dicetylphosphate or phosphatidic acid in molar ratios 7:2:1. The negative
charge of the liposomes so constituted can be replaced by a positive
charge by substituting stearylamine for dicetylphosphate. Increasing
the ratio of cholesterol to phospholipid results in the formation
of liposomes more stable at body temperature. Proteins or other water-
soluble antigens added to the electrolyte solution are entrapped in
the liposomes, and the entrapped and free material are separated by
passing the liposomes through a Sephadex column. The efficiency of
entrapment can be monitored by labelling the antigen, e.g. by iodination of proteins with radioactive iodine: it is often about 50%, but
with some materials may fall to 20% or occasionally less. Lipid-solu-
ble antigens, such as gangliosides, can be incorporated into the lipid
phase of liposomes.

The structure of a liposome is shown diagramatically in Fig. 1. X-ray
diffraction of liposomes shows the existence of multilamellar structures with repeating distances varying from 54Å-75Å depending on the
lipid used (8). Electron micrographs of liposomes show each bilayer
to be approximately 50Å thick (3).

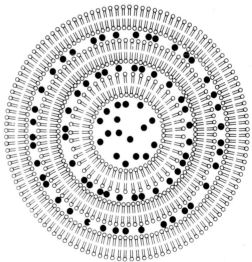

● ●   Aqueous compartment containing antigen

⋔⋔⋔   Phospholipid bilayer

*Fig. 1. Diagrammatic representation of a cross section of liposome,
showing concentric phospholipid bilayers alternating with aqueous
compartments containing a hydrosoluble antigen.*

Table 1. Serum antibody responses of mice to DT administered free or in liposomes of different compositions (2)

| Experimental group | No. of mice | Mode of administration | Route of administration | Primary Ab response | Secondary Ab response | Probability |
|---|---|---|---|---|---|---|
| a | 15 | Free | i.v. | 1.8 | – | a v b $p < 0.01$ |
| b | 15 | Liposomes (PA) | i.v. | 10.0 | – | |
| c | 6 | Free | s.c. | 2.5 | 11.6 | a v d $p < 0.01$ |
| d | 6 | Liposomes (PA) | s.c. | 6.7 | 13.3 | d v e $p < 0.01$ |
| e | 6 | Liposomes | s.c. | 0 | 11.3 | c v e $p < 0.10$ |
| f | 6 | Free | i.m. | 1.7 | 7.5 | f v g $p < 0.10$ |
| g | 6 | Liposomes (PA) | i.m. | 3.7 | 11.0 | g v h $p < 0.05$ |
| h | 6 | Liposomes | i.m. | 6.6 | 12.0 | f v h $p < 0.01$ |

Mice were of the TO strain, except in groups c to e, which were of the CBA strain. Positive (+) liposomes (0.5 mg lipid) were composed of egg lecithin, cholesterol and stearylamine in molar ratios 7:2:1; in negative (−) liposomes phosphatidic acid (PA) or diacetylphosphate (DP) replaced stearylamine. Primary serum antibody responses were measured after 13 or 14 days, booster injections with 20 μg antigen in the same form were given and secondary responses were measured after a further 10 days (groups c to e) or 14 days (groups f to h). Antibody responses were measured by indirect haemagglutination and expressed as the $\log_2$ IH titre.

# ANTIBODY RESPONSES TO ANTIGENS ENTRAPPED IN LIPOSOMES

Our first experiments were performed with diphtheria toxoid (DT) because it is an antigen which is administered to humans, can be con-
veniently labelled with radioactive iodine and is readily incorporated
into liposomes; the formation of antibodies can be measured easily by
passive haemagglutination. Representative observations on mice immunized with free and liposome-entrapped DT by the i.v. and s.c. routes
are presented in Table 1 (2). DT administered i.v. in negatively charged
liposomes elicits the formation of much higher concentrations of antibodies than are elicited by free antigen. Subcutaneous (footpad) inoculation of DT in negatively charged liposomes elicits significantly
higher primary and secondary antibody responses than the same dose of
free antigen. In contrast, antigen entrapped in positively charged
liposomes elicits less antibody than the same dose of free antigen.
Intramuscular injection of DT in negatively charged liposomes again
elicits significantly higher antibody levels than free DT (Table 1).
In these and other experiments, dicetylphosphate-containing liposomes
as adjuvants were superior to those containing phosphatidic acid.

Mice immunized with DT in liposomes challenged by footpad injection
of DT showed Arthus (6h) reactions but not delayed hypersensitivity
(24-72 h reactions). When immune mice were inoculated i.v. with free
DT they developed severe serum-sickness reactions, and the majority
died. In contrast, the same amount of antigen entrapped in liposomes
inoculated s.c. or i.v. into immune animals did not elicit Arthus or
serum-sickness reactions. Thus, entrapment of antigens in liposomes
facilitates the increase of antibody responses in animals that are
already immune without danger of hypersensitivity (5).

# COMBINATION OF LIPOSOME-ENTRAPPED ANTIGEN AND BACTERIAL OR OTHER AD-
JUVANTS

When protein antigens are administered together with heat-killed Mycobacterium tuberculosis or Bortedella pertussis increased antibody responses and delayed hypersensitivity are found. Experiments were performed to ascertain the effect of administration of liposome-entrapped
DT together with killed M.tuberculosis or B.pertussis. Representative

Table 2. Effect of liposome (DP) entrapment of DT with and without
BCG on primary and secondary responses

| | Mode of antigen administation | Primary response (IHA) | Secondary response (IHA) |
|---|---|---|---|
| a | Free | O | 12.6 |
| b | Free + BCG | O | 14.4 |
| c | Liposomes (DP) | 1.4 | 12.8 |
| d | Liposomes (DP)+BCG | 7.2 (c v d) ($p$ < 0.01) | 17.4 (c v d) ($p$ < 0.01) |

Groups of 5 VSBS/NIMR mice were infected i.m. with 20 µg DT free or
liposome-entrapped with or without admixture of heat-killed BCG. Mice
were bled after 14 days, reinoculated with 20 µg DT without BCG and
bled again 10 days later.

results are shown in Tables 2 and 3. In both cases the primary and secondary antibody responses were significantly increased in the presence of the bacteria.

When protein antigens or viruses are administrated in the presence of the surface-active saponin, antibody responses are increased. The experiments summarized in Table 4 show that addition of saponin to liposome with entrapped DT further increases the antibody response to the toxin.

Table 3. Effect of liposome entrapment of DT with or without *B. pertussis* (BP) organisms on primary and secondary antibody responses

|   | Mode of antigen administration | Primary response (IHA) | Probability | Secondary response (IHA) | Probability |
|---|---|---|---|---|---|
| a | Free | 8.0 | | 12.0 | |
| b | Free + BP | 10.2 | a v b $p < 0.01$ | 15.4 | a v b $p < 0.01$ |
| c | Liposomes (DP) | 10.0 | a v c $p < 0.01$ | 15.6 | |
| d | Liposomes (DP)+ BP | 11.5 | a v d $p < 0.01$ | 19.7 | a v d $p < 0.01$ |

Groups of 5 VSBS/NIMR mice were inoculated with 20 µg DT free or liposome-entrapped, with and without admixture of killed B. pertussis organisms. Mice were bled after 14 days, reinoculated with 20 µg DT without bacteria and bled again after a further 13 days.

Table 4. Effect of saponin on immune responses to liposome-entrapped DT

| Mode of antigen administration | Primary response (IHA) | Secondary response (IHA) |
|---|---|---|
| Free | O | 5.4 |
| Liposomes (DP) | O | 7.5 |
| Liposomes (DP) + 3 g saponin | O | 6.5 |
| Liposomes (DP) + 50 g saponin | O | 12.6 ($p < 0.01$) |

Groups of 5 VSBS/NIMR mice were inoculated with 20 µg DT, free or liposome-entrapped, with or without saponin (3 and 20 µg). Primary antibody responses were determined after 13 days, animals were inoculated with 20 µg antigen without saponin and secondary antibody responses measured after 13 days.

## DISCUSSION

Liposomes appear to have promise as vehicles for the administration
of antigens. Their preparation is straightforward, and not much more
time-consuming than the preparation of conventional adjuvants. Water-
soluble antigens, such as proteins, can be entrapped in the aqueous
compartments of liposomes and lipod-soluble antigens, such as glyco-
lipids, in their lipid bilayers. From quite extensive results in our
laboratory, of which a few with DT have been given here as examples,
it is clear that liposomes increase antibody responses to a variety
of protein antigens, including viral antigens. The charge of the liposome is certainly important: proteins having positive charges at pH
7.0-7.4, such as lysozyme, are more immunogenic in positively charged
than negatively charged liposomes. Other features affecting the stability of liposomes, such as the lecithin-cholesterol ratio, may also
prove to be important and are under investigation in our laboratory.
Homing of liposomes to macrophages might be promoted by the use of
denatured immunoglobulin or activated C3 on their surface, and this
may increase immunogenicity. No granulomas are formed at the sites
of injection of liposomes, unlike the sites of injection of conventional adjuvants. Studies with labelled antigens show relatively rapid
mobilization from the injection site with remarkably high retention
in the draining lymph nodes. Liposomes have been injected into human
subjects without any ill effects.

It is already clear that when other materials with adjuvant activity
such as M.tuberculosis, B.pertussis or saponin, are injected together
with antigen in liposomes, immune responses are augmented. Experiments
are in progress with other materials, including water-soluble deriva-
tives of mycobacterial cell walls kindly supplied by Doctors CHEDID
and JOLLES. Some of the latter have been shown to increase the activity
of macrophages against tumour cells (6), and administration of these
in liposomes may provide a convenient way of increasing host resistance against tumours.

Our ultimate aim with respect to immunotherapy of tumours in human
patients is to administer tumour antigen preparations (preferably purified plasma-membrane-glycoprotein or glycolipid fractions) in liposomes together with an agent that has adjuvant effects - increasing
specific immune responses to the tumour antigens and at the same time
increasing non-specific immunity against tumours mediated by macrophages and other cells. Since liposomes are biodegradable and do not
provoke any reaction at the site of injection, and the recently in-
troduced adjuvants are non-toxic and are not themselves immunogenic,
we hope that good immunostimulation will be achieved without any adverse effect on the patients.

## REFERENCES

1. Allison, A.C.: Effects of adjuvants on different cell types and
   their interactions in immune responses. In: Immunopotentiation,
   Ciba Foundation Symposium No. 18 (new series). (Amsterdam) Associated Scientific Publishers (1973) pp.72-94
2. Allison, A.C., Gregoriadis, G.: Liposomes as immunological adjuvants. Nature (Lond.) 252, 252 (1974)
3. Bangham, A.D.: Membrane models with phospholipids. Progr. Biophys.
   Molec. Biol. 18, 29-95 (1968)

4. Bangham, A.D., Standish, M.M., Watkins, J.C.: Diffusion of univalent ions across the lamellae of swollen phospholipids. J. Mol. Biol. 13, 238-252 (1965)
5. Gregoriadis, G., Allison, A.C.: Entrapment of proteins in liposomes prevents allergic reactions in pre-immunized mice. FEBS Letters 45, 71-74 (1974)
6. Juy, D., Bona, C., Chedid, L.: Effect antitumoral de macrophages peritoneux activés par un adjuvant hydrosoluble d'origine mycobacterienne. C.R. Acad. Sci. (Paris) 278, 2859-2862 (1974)
7. Paphadjopoulos, D., Miller, N.: Phospholipid model membranes. I. Structural characteristics of hydrated liquid crystals. Biochim. Biophys. Acta 135, 624-638 (1967)
8. Paphadjopoulos, D., Watkins, J.C.: Phospholipid model membranes. II. Permeability properties of hydrated liquid crystals. Biochim. Biophys. Acta 135, 639-652 (1967)

# Chapter 9
# Nonspecific Immunodepression Induced by Tumor-Cell Extracts*

R. HUCHET and J. LHERITIER

Immunodepression in mice bearing tumors or injected with tumor cells or tumor-cell products is relevant to different mechanisms according to the experimental model used. In Rauscher and Friend leukemias the immunodepression is due to the oncogenic virus itself (1, 13); on the other hand, in the case of tumors which have no viral etiology (Ehrlich tumor, Lewis tumor, or chemically induced tumors) several factors isolated from the tumor cells or ascite fluid were shown to have suppressive properties (3, 7, 8, 10, 11, 15, 16).

The nature of the factors was either a γ-globulin (11), or products of different molecular weight (15, 16), or undetermined. BONMASSAR et al. (2) described another factor isolated from transplantable mouse leukemia which had immunodepressive properties similar to those of the lacticodehydrogenase elevating virus (LDV), which is a usual contaminant of many transplantable tumors. These authors suggested that this nononcogenic virus could be one of the etiologic agents of the immunodepression observed in their experiments.

We studied the immunodepression induced by tumor-cell extracts (Lewis tumor and chemically induced tumor). The results of these studies reported here suggest that a nononcogenic virus could be the main factor responsible for the immunodepression observed.

## MATERIAL AND METHODS

### Mice

F1 hybrids (DBA/2 x C57Bl/6) and A/J mice from CNRS breeding center (Orléans, France) were used when 8-10 weeks old.

### Cell Lines

Lewis tumor and L 1210 were maintained by serial passage on F1 hybrids.

Dimethylbenzanthracene (DMBA)-induced leukemia was produced in newborn F1 hybrid by injecting 50 μg DMBA i.p.. Leukemia (which is referred to as L20, L21, L22, L23) appeared 2 months later, and were characterized

* This work was sponsored by Grant (No. 352) from Université Paris Sud (UER Kremlim Bicêtre).

by spleen and lymph-node localizations. The leukemic cells were used after one passage on F1 hybrids.

Tumor-cell suspensions from Lewis tumor and spleens from leukemic mice, adjusted to contain $2.10^7$ cells per ml, were either irradiated (15,000r given by a cobalt source) or frozen and thawed three times. 0.5 ml of the suspension was injected i.p. into the normal F1 recipient.

## Antigens and Immunization

The following 2,4,6 trinitrophenyl conjugates, TNP-polymer of Flagelline ($TNP_2$-POL) and TNP hemocyanin ($TNP_{20}$-KLH), were prepared as described by RITTENBERG (12). Subscripts refer to the average number of moles of TNP per monomer of POL or per 100,000 g of KLH. Immunization was carried out with 50 µg of TNP-POL in saline i.p., and 500 µg of TNP-KLH emulsified in complete Freund adjuvant.

## Measurement of the Anti-TNP Response

Tne anti-TNP response was measured by the number of plaque-forming cells (PFC) per spleen determined by CUNNINGHAM's technique (4). PFC are referred as direct or indirect PFC. The latter are revealed by the use of rabbit anti-mouse PFC.

## Spleen-Cell Stimulation by PHA

Culture conditions for PHA stimulation were described by FLORENTIN (6). The response is expressed by the absolute count per minute of tritiated thymidine incorporated per culture.

## Skin Graft

The skin graft was performed according to the technique of TENENBAUM (14).

All the results are expressed by the arithmetic mean at its 95% confidence limits. Comparisons between means were performed according to the Student's-t-test.

## RESULTS

### IMMUNE STATUS OF MICE GIVEN LEWIS TUMOR CELL EXTRACTS

F1 hybrids, which were given 0.5 ml of Lewis tumor cell suspension containing $2.10^7$ irradiated or frozen thawed cells i.p., were tested after 2 weeks.

### A/J Skin Grafts

The mean duration of H2 histoincompatible skin graft from A/J (H2a) on F1 hybrid (H2d H2b) was 11.8 days $\pm$ 3.1 in the control group and 21 days $\pm$ 4.3 (Table 1) in the treated group. The difference is statistically significant (p < 0.05) (Table 1).

### PHA Responsiveness

There is complete abolition of PHA responsiveness of the spleen cells of the treated group, as shown in Fig. 1. There is no tritiated thymidine incorporation. These results contrast with those obtained in the control group where the $^{3}$H-thymidine incorporation expressed by the total count per culture was found to be between 100,000 and 140,000 cpm. The spontaneous incorporation was also depressed in the treated group.

Table 1. Effect of pretreatment of F1 (DBA/2 x C/57) hybrid mice with irradiated Lewis tumor cells, on A/J skin allograft survival

| Control | Treated |
|---|---|
| 11.8 ± 3.1 days[a] | 21.4 ± 4.3 days[a] |

[a] $p < 0.05$.

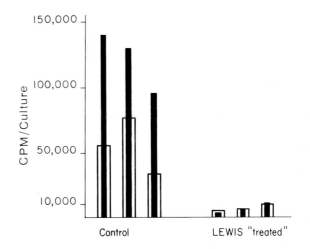

Fig. 1. PHA responsiveness of spleen cells from normal and Lewis-treated cells expressed by tritiated thymidine incorporation (dpm per culture). White bars: Spontaneous $^{3}$H-thymidine incorporation. Black bars: Incorporation of $^{3}$H thymidine of cells cultured in presence of PHA

Anti-TNP Response to TNP-KLH

There is a complete abolition of the IgG response (indirect PFC) at day 8 in the treated groups, whereas the mean number of the PFC in the control is 30,000 ± 10,000 (Table 2).

This abolition of the IgG response in the treated mice was found whenever IgG antibody plaque-forming cells were observed in the control.

Anti-TNP Response to TNP-POL

The anti-TNP response to the thymus-independent antigen TNP-POL was similar in the control and in the treated group (Table 2). This response demonstrates the integrity of the B-cell functions.

We can therefore conclude that the depression of immunity induced by Lewis tumor cells affects the expression of T-cell functions as shown

67

by the delayed skin-graft rejection, the abolition of PHA responsiveness, the abolition of the anti-TNP response to the thymus-dependent
antigen TNP-KLH, contrasting with the normal response to TNP-POL which
demonstrates the integrity of the B cells. However, we cannot distinguish which cell is altered: T cells, macrophages, or both.

Table 2. Effect of pretreatment of FA(DBA/2 x C/57) hybrid mice with
irradiated or frozen thawed Lewis tumor cells on the anti TNP response

| Antigen used | | Control group | Treated group |
|---|---|---|---|
| TNP-KLH (500 μ in CFA i.p.) | Indirect PFC per spleen at day 7 | 30,000 ± 11,000 | 0 |
| TNP-POL (50 μg in saline i.p.) | Direct PFC per spleen at day 5 | 3,600 ± 1,500 | 4,400 ± 900 |

## IMMUNE STATUS OF MICE GIVEN DMBA LEUKEMIC CELL EXTRACTS

In order to check if similar results could be obtained with recently
induced tumor, we used the DMBA leukemia (L20, L21, L22, L23) according to a protocol similar to that used with the Lewis tumor cells.

F1 hybrids which had been given the tumor cells were challenged with
TNP-KLH 2 weeks later.

The results are expressed in Table 3: with two tumors (L20 and L23)
there is practically a complete abolition of the anti-TNP responses.
With the other two tumors (L21 and L22) the number of indirect PFC
per spleen is 2000 ± 1800 and 6000 ± 5000 respectively, versus 77,000
± 15,000 in the controls.

Table 3. Anti TNP response to TNP KLH, of F1 (DBA/2 x C/57) hybrid
mice treated with frozen thawed DMBA tumor cells 14 days prior to
antigen injection

| | Control | L20 | L21 | L22 | L23 |
|---|---|---|---|---|---|
| Indirect PFC/spleen at day 7 | 77,000 ± 15,000[a] | 700 ± 600[a] | 2000 ± 1800[a] | 6000 ± 5000[a] | 500 ± 200[a] |

[a] $p < 1‰$

## STUDY OF THE NATURE OF THE IMMUNODEPRESSION

In order to obtain insight into the nature of the immunodepression,
tumor-cell extracts (Lewis tumor cells or DMBA leukemic cells) corresponding to $2.10^7$ cells per ml, were treated at $56°$ for 30 min, or
passed through a millipore filter (0.22 μ), and then injected into

Table 4. Effect of the administration of frozen thawed liver cells or thymus cells from normal mice or from mice given Lewis tumor cell extracts 14 days before, on the anti-TNP response to the TNP-KLH[a] (500 µg in CFA i.p.)

| Indirect PFC per spleen at day 7 | No treatment | $10^8$ frozen thawed thymus cells from normal mice | $10^7$ frozen thawed liver cells from normal mice | Serum (1 ml) from normal mice | $10^8$ frozen thawed thymus cells from mice given Lewis tumor cells 14 days before | $10^7$ frozen thawed liver cells from mice given Lewis tumor cells 14 days before | Serum 1 ml from treated mice |
|---|---|---|---|---|---|---|---|
| | 248,000 ± 50,000 | 210,000 ± 40,000[b] | 190,000 ± 71,000[c] | 227,000 ± 62,000 | 17,000 ± 3,500[b] | 21,000 ± 10,000[c] | 254,000 ± 26,000 |

[a] TNP-KLH given 14 days after the cell-extract injection.

[b,c] $p < 1‰$

normal F1 hybrids which were given TNP-KLH two weeks later. These procedures did not alter the pattern of the depression of the anti-TNP response (results not given here).The depression on anti-TNP response induced by a filtrate of DMBA leukemic cells was still persistent 6 weeks after injection of the filtrate.

In order to eliminate the possibility that such an immunodepression could be due to an oncogenic virus present in the DMBA leukemic cells, mice which were given the filtrate were kept under observation for 10 months: no clinical sign or expression of malignancy or leukemia were observed.

Finally the transmission of the immunodepression was studied.

Frozen thawed cells of different organs from normal mice or from mice which had been given tumoral extracts from Lewis tumor, were injected into normal recipients which were given TNP-KLH two weeks later. The results are expressed in Table 4.

Mice injected with thymus or liver cells from nontreated mice give an anti-TNP response similar to that of the control which did not receive any cell injection: (210,000 ± 40,000) and 190,000 ± 71,000 indirect PFC per spleen in the group given $10^8$ thymus cell and $10^7$ liver cells respectively, versus 248,000 ± 50,000 in the group where no cells were given). On the other hand, mice which had been given thymus or liver cells from treated mice showed a severe impairement of the anti-TNP response: 17,000 ± 3,500 indirect PFC and 21,000 ± 10,000 in the group given $10^8$ thymus cell and $10^7$ liver cells respectively. No transmission of the immunodepression was found with the serum of the treated mice.

Similar results were observed with recipients given thymus-cell or liver-cell extracts from mice treated with DMBA leukemic-cell extracts. (Results not given here.)

CONCLUSIONS

The immunodepression induced by tumor extracts in these experiments is characterized by the severe impairement of cell-mediated immunity, meaning an alteration of T-cell or macrophage functions or both. This depression is specific to tumor cells and is observed with normal tissue extracts. This model is different from that observed with Ehrlich ascites (7) where the function of the B cells is impaired. The transmission of the immunodepression by thymus-cell or liver-cell extracts of treated mice rules out the involvement of factors like those described by PIKOVSKI (11) and YAMAZAKI (16). On the other hand, the role of suppressor cells in the etiology of the immuno-suppression (5,9) cannot be completely eliminated.

Finally, our experimental model seems to us to favor the role of a self-replicating agent (a nononcogenic virus) and is compatible with that described by BONMASSAR (2).

REFERENCES

1. Bennet, M., Steeves, R.A.: Immunocompetent functions in mice infected with Friend leukemia virus. J. Nat. Cancer Inst. 44, 1107 (1970)
2. Bonmassar, E., Bonmassar, A., Goldin, A., Cudkovicz, G.: Depression of anti-lymphoma allograft reactivity by tumor associated factors. Cancer Res. 33, 1054 (1973)
3. Chan, P.L., Sinclair, N.R. Stc.: Immunologic and virologic properties of chemically and γ-irradiation induced thymic lymphomas in mice. J. Nat. Cancer Inst. 48, 1629 (1972)
4. Cunningham, A.J., Szenberg, A.: Further improvements on the plaque technique for detecting single antibody forming cells. Immunol. 14, 599 (1968)
5. Eggers, A.E., Wunderlich, J.A.: Suppressor cells in tumor bearing mice capable of non specific blocking of in vitro immunisation against transplant antigens. J. Immunol. 114, 1554 (1975)
6. Florentin, I., Kiger, N.: Stimulatory effects of a calf thymic extract on the PHA responsiveness of bone marrow cells. Europ. J. Clin. Biol. Res. 17, 597 (1972)
7. Hrsak, I., Marotti, T.: Immunosuppression mediated by Ehrlich ascite fluid. Europ. J. Cancer 9, 717 (1973)
8. Kamo, I., Patel, L., Kateley, J., Friedman, M.: Immunosuppression induced in vitro by mastocytoma tumor cells and cell free extracts. J. Immunol. 114, 1749 (1975)
9. Kirchner, M., Chused, T.M., Herberman, R.B., Holden, H.T., Lavrin, D.M.: Evidence of suppressor cell activity in spleen of mice bearing primary tumors induced by moloney sarcoma virus. J. Exp. Med. 139, 1473 (1974)
10. Mc Carty, R.E., Coffin, J.M., Gates, S.L.: Selective inhibition of the secondary immune response to mouse skin allografts by cell free Ehrlich ascites carcinoma fluid. Transplantation 6, 737 (1968)
11. Pikovski, M.A., Ziffroni-Gallon, Y., Witz, I.P.: Suppression of immune response to sheep red blood cells in mice treated with preparations of a tumor cells component and in tumor bearing mice. Europ. J. Immunol. 5, 447 (1975)
12. Rittenberg, M.B., Amkraut, A.A.: Immunogenicity of trinitrophenyl hemocyanin: production of primary and secondary anti-hapten precipitins. J. Immunol. 97, 421 (1966)
13. Siegel, B.V., Morton, J.I.: Deprssed antibody response in the mouse infected with Rauscher leukemia virus. Immunol. 10, 559 (1966)
14. Tennenbaum, R., Mery, A.M., Amiel, J.L., Mathe, G.: Nouvelle technique de greffe de peau chez la souris. Rev. Franc. Et. Clin. et Biol. 6, 1106 (1961)
15. Wong, A., Mankovitz, R., Kennedy, J.L.: Immunosuppressive and immunostimulatory factors produced by malignant cells in vitro. Int. J. Cancer 13, 530 (1974)
16. Yamazaki, H., Nitta, K., Umezawa, H.: Immunosuppression induced with cell free fluid of Ehrlich carcinoma ascites and its fractions. Gann. 64, 83 (1973)

# Chapter 10

## Increase in "Null" Cells in Acute Lymphocytic Leukemia in Remission on Long-Term Immunotherapy

R. R. JOSEPH and D. BELPOMME

INTRODUCTION

In the last decade, many reports have attested to the clinical bene-
fits of immunotherapy in the treatment of malignant diseases. Extensive reviews of these publications have recently appeared (6, 12). Although experimental evidence regarding the mechanism of action of BCG
and/or inactivated tumor cells on animal immune systems is abundant
(7, 8, 11, 13, 15), consistent data in humans is still scanty.

The purpose of the present study is to evaluate the effect of such a
therapeutic program on the circulating mononuclear cell population
in patients in complete remission from acute lymphocytic leukemia (ALL).
To this end, we compared a group of patients on long-term immunotherapy to a similar group receiving standard maintenance chemotherapy
and to a group of normal individuals.

MATERIALS AND METHODS

Patients

Thirty-one patients with ALL currently in remission were studied. At
the time they were tested 20 of these were receiving immunotherapy
and 11 chemotherapy. Immunotherapy consisted of fresh, living BCG
(Pasteur) administered by scarification at intervals ranging from
once weekly to once monthly and irradiated, formalized allogenic blast
cells ($10^8$) administered intradermal monthly (10). Chemotherapy
consisted of weekly methotrexate (i.m., 15 mgm/m$^2$) and cyclophosphamide
(200 mgm/m$^2$) plus daily 6-mercaptopurine (p.o., 50 mgm/m$^2$). Precise
dosage was adjusted weekly according to the level of neutrophils.
These patients were compared with nine normal subjects as controls.

A summary of the age and sex distribution, plus the duration of maintenance treatment is presented in Table 1. Although the patients investigated were drawn from several different protocols operational
over the years, all such protocols consist of a period of post-induc-
tion chemotherapy followed by immunotherapy. Accordingly, the immunotherapy group had received a variable period of post-remission chemotherapy and then a period of immunotherapy ranging, as seen on Table 1,
from 13-96 months. The patients in the chemotherapy group are those
who have not yet completed the chemotherapy phase of the current ALL
protocol and have been treated for periods ranging from 3-14 months.

Table 1. Study groups (ALL in complete remission)

| | Number of patients | Sex | Age (mean + range) | Duration of maintenance treatment (mean + range) |
|---|---|---|---|---|
| Chemotherapy | 11 | 10 M 1 F | 10.1 years (5-31) | 8.9 months (3-14) |
| Immunotherapy[a] | 20 | 7 M 13 F | 11.5 years (4-21) | 28.2 months (13-96) |
| Normals | 9 | 4 M 5 F | 30 years (20-50) | |

[a] Post-chemotherapy.

## Laboratory Procedures

Total and differential white-cell counts were performed on all subjects. The absolute number of each category of cells was calculated by multiplying the percentages obtained in the following procedures by the absolute number of mononuclear cells.

Peripheral blood was collected in citrate from each subject and the mononuclear cells isolated and purified by a previously described Ficoll gradient procedure (1). A preparation of 99% pure mononuclear cells was obtained by this method. After at least three washings, these cells were used in the tests described below.

## T-Lymphocytes

T-lymphocytes were enumerated by the E-rosette test using sheep red blood cells (SRBC). Rosettes were defined as lymphocytes surrounded by at least three SRBC. We performed this test in two ways. In the first, or direct test, rosettes resulting from the incubation of mononuclear cells and SRBC alone were counted (ERFC). In the second, or AB serum test, AB human serum, previously decomplemented and absorbed with sheep RBC was added to the incubation mixture (EABRFC). We, as others, have previously shown that this latter procedure gives a higher number of rosettes than the former (1, 3) and we have confirmed this observation in our current work (Table 2). This phenomenon may be related to the detection of the total number of T cells by the sensitized test, while the direct test may define a subpopulation of this group.

## B-Lymphocytes

Enumeration of B-lymphocytes was performed by determination of membrane immunoglobulin (mIg) using a direct immunofluorescent test with a polyvalent fluorescent isothiocyanate conjugated sheep anti-human immunoglobulin serum. Details of this method have been previously described (1).

Table 2. Comparison of rosette formation with or without serum AB

| | E R F C | | E A B R F C | |
|---|---|---|---|---|
| | % | No. | % | No. |
| Chemotherapy | 35 | 496 | 42 | 696 |
| Immunotherapy | 32 | 869 | 44 | 1173 |
| Normals | 46 | 1074 | 56 | 1299 |

## Monocytes

Monocytes were enumerated by peroxidase staining as suggested by a recent W.H.O. Workshop (18). One thousand mononuclear cells were counted for peroxidase positivity on each slide.

## "Null" Cells

After establishing the absolute number of each of the three foregoing groups (EABRFC, mIg positive cells, peroxidase positive cells) we calculated the number of so-called null cells by the following formula: Null cells = mononuclear cells - (EABRFC + mIg positive cells + peroxidase positive cells).

## Statistical Analysis

Statistical analysis were performed using the Student's-t-test.

## RESULTS

Table 3 presents a summary of the results of our study and their statistical significance.

## Chemotherapy Group

The patients on chemotherapy had a significant reduction in the mean number of mononuclear cells and of the total number of EABRFC in comparison to both the immunotherapy and normal groups. No such difference was noted in either the total number of mIg positive or peroxidase positive cells. When null cells were calculated no difference to normal cells was found, but there were far fewer (p = 0.001) in this group than in the patients receiving immunotherapy.

## Immunotherapy Group

As discussed above, the immunotherapy patients had a significant elevation of mononuclear cells, EABRFC cells, and "null" cells over the chemotherapy group. Although there were differences in the total

Table 3. Summary of results

| | Mononuclear cells | EABRFC | mIg Positive | Peroxidase positive | "Null" |
|---|---|---|---|---|---|
| Chemotherapy | 1470 | 696 | 455 | 344 | 104 (7%[a]) |
| Immunotherapy | 2714 | 1173 | 467 | 198 | 883 (33%[a]) |
| Normal | 2356 | 1299 | 381 | 396 | 304 (12%[a]) |
| Chemotherapy/ Immunotherapy | $p = < 0.001$ | $p = 0.01$ | N.S. | N.S. | $p = < 0.001$ |
| Normal/Chemo- therapy | $p = 0.02$ | $p = 0.01$ | N.S. | N.S. | N.S. |
| Normal/Immuno- therapy | N.S. | N.S. | N.S. | N.S. | $p = < 0.01$ |

[a] Percent mononuclear cells without markers.

number of mononuclear cells and of the subpopulations between the immunotherapy and normal group, the only statistically significant difference was in the calculated null cells. There was a much larger number of such cells in the immunotherapy group (p = 0.01).

## DISCUSSION

In our study the percentage and total number of EABRFC, mIg positive, and peroxidase positive cells in normal individuals were in the range previously published (20). The calculated null cells are also in agreement with available data. Our control group was composed of subjects in an older age group than our patient groups because of the logistic difficulty of obtaining normal pediatric subjects. Several recent reports give conflicting results on the influence of age on the distribution of B and T cells. WEKSLER and HUTHEFORTH (17), for example, found no change in the absolute number of peripheral lymphocytes or T and B cells with increasing age, and CAROSELLA (4) demonstrated a decreased percentage of T cells occurring somewhere between 46 and 60 years of age. Since our control group had a mean age (30 years) considerably younger than this we believe that age difference does not represent a significant problem in the analysis of our results.

The chemotherapy group was marked by a diminution in total mononuclear cell count. Surprisingly, our data showed that this decrease involved the T- rather than B-lymphocytes. Immunoglobulin levels were consistent with our "B cell" results, in that the chemotherapy group did not vary significantly in its IgG, IgA, or IgM values compared to the normal group. These findings differ from those reported by SEN and BORELLA (16) who found that T cells were in the normal range while B cells were decreased in patients with ALL on the last day of a 3-year chemotherapy program. Although the difference in results remains unexplained, the shorter period of chemotherapy in our patients (8.9 months) may in part account for this discrepancy.

A striking finding of our study is the significant elevation in the absolute number and percentage of "null" cells in the immunotherapy group as compared with both the chemotherapy and normal groups. Although the nature of these cells is still unknown, several hypothesis concerning their increase in this situation can be entertained.

1. The cells may represent abnormal elements persisting even during apparently complete remission of ALL. The continued perfect clinical and cytological condition of these patients does not favor this hypothesis.

2. They may be stem cells circulating in the peripheral blood. Although it has been demonstrated that BCG can increase hematopoietic stem cells in mouse bone marrow (14) human data is lacking.

3. They may be "K" cells. It has been shown that there is increased "K" cell activity in patients on BCG therapy for ALL in comparison to patients receiving no treatment (9). This hypothesis seems plausible since it has recently been suggested that "K" cells may be "null" cells (5).

4. They may represent T- or B-lymphocytes or monocytes which have lost any detectable markers, a change possibly induced by immunotherapy.

5. A final possibility is that there may not be a true increase in these cells, but rather a redistribution between the peripheral blood and the various reticulo-endothelial organs.

Further studies are in progress in our laboratory to confirm these preliminary results and to elucidate the nature of these intriguing cells.

## Acknowledgments

We gratefully acknowledge the technical cooperation of Danièle Grandjon and the statistical assistance of G. Hauss. Supported by grants from I.N.S.E.R.M. ATP 107431.

## SUMMARY

In an attempt to elucidate a possible mode of action of immunotherapy in ALL, we studied the mononuclear subpopulation in a group of patients with ALL in remission on long-term immunotherapy, a similar group on chemotherapy, and a group of normal individuals.

Comparison of the three groups demonstrated a significant increase in the number and percentage of "null" cells in the immunotherapy group relative to the two others. Although the nature of these cells is unknown, the possibilities that they represent persistent abnormal elements, circulating stem cells, "K" cells, or modified T, B, or monocytic cells are raised.

## REFERENCES

1. Belpomme, D., Dantchev, D., Du Rusquec, E., Grandjon, D., Huchet, R., Pouillart, P., Schwarzenberg, L., Amiel, J.L., Mathé, G.: T and B lymphocyte markers on the neoplastic cell of 20 patients with acute and 10 patients with chronic lymphoid leukemia. Biomed. 20, 109 (1974)
2. Belpomme, D., Dantchev, D., Joseph, R., Santoro, A., Feuilhade de Chauvin, F., Lelarge, N., Grandjon, D., Ponvert, D., Mathé, G.: Classification of leukemias and hematosarcomas based on cell membrane markers and scanning electron microscopy. In: Clinical tumour immunology. Oxford: Pergamon Press, 1976, Vol. I, p. 131
3. Bentwich, Z., Douglas, S.D., Siegal, F.P., Kunkel, H.G.: Human lymphocyte-sheep erythrocyte rosette formation: some characteristics of the interaction. Clin. Immunol. Immunoth. Pathol. 1, 511-522 (1973)
4. Carosella, E.D., Mochanko, K., Brown, M.: Rosette forming T-cells in human peripheral blood at different ages. Cell Immunol. 12, 323-325 (1974)
5. Greenberg, A.H., Hudsen, L., Shen, L., Roitt, I.M.: Antibody-dependent cell-mediated cytotoxicity due to a "null" lymphoid cell. Nature (New Biol.) 242, 111 (1973)
6. Guttermann, J.U., Navligit, G.M., Reed, R.C., Hersh, E.M.: Immunochemotherapy of human cancer. Seminars in Oncology 1, 409 (1974)
7. Halpern, B.N., Biozzi, G., Stiffel, C., Mouton, D.: Effet de la stimulation du système réticulo-endothélial par l'inoculation du bacille Calmette-Guérin sur le développement de l'épithélioma atypique T-8 de Guérin chez le rat. C.R. Soc. Biol. Paris, 153, 919 (1959)

8. Mackaness, G.B., Auclair, D.J., Lagrande, P.H.: Immunopotentiation with BCG I. Immune response to different strains and preparations. J. Nat. Cancer Inst. 51, 1655 (1973)

9. Mac Lennan, I.C.M.: Immunosuppression and immunostimulation in acute leukemia. Proc. Roy. Soc. Med. 68, 216 (1975)

10. Mathé, G., Amiel, J.L., Schwarzenberg, L., Schneider, M., Cattan, A., Schlumberger, J.R., Hayat, M., De Vassal, F.: Active immunotherapy for acute lymphoid leukemia. Lancet 1, 697 (1969)

11. Mathé, G., Kamel, M., Dezfulian, M., Halle-Pannenko, Bourut, C.: An experimental screening for "systemic adjuvands of immunity" applicable in cancer immunotherapy. Cancer Res. 33, 1987 (1973)

12. Nathanson, L.: Use of BCG in the treatment of human neoplasms: a review. Seminars in Oncology 1, 337 (1974)

13. Old, L.J., Benacerraf, B., Clarke, D.A., Carswell, E.A., Stockert, E.: The role of the reticuloendothelial system in the host reaction to neoplasia. Cancer Res. 21, 1281-1300 (1961)

14. Pouillart, P., Palangie, T., Schwarzenberg, L., Brugerie, E., Lhéritier, J., Mathé, G.: Effect of BCG on hematopoietic stem cells: experimental and clinical study. Cancer Immunol. Immunoth., in press (1976)

15. Reif, A.E., Kim, C.A.H.: Leukemia L1210 therapy trials with antileukemia serum and Bacillus Calmette-Guérin. Cancer Res. 31, 1606-1612 (1971)

16. Sen, L., Borella, L.: Expression of cell surface markers on T and B lymphocytes after long-term chemotherapy of acute leukemia. Cell. Immunol. 9, 84 (1973)

17. Weksler, M.E., Hutteroth, .: Impaired lymphocyte function in aged humans. J. Clin. Invest. 53, 99-104 (1974)

18. W.H.O./I.A.R.C. Workshops: Special technical report. Identification, enumeration and isolation of B and T lymphocytes from human peripheral blood. Scand. J. Immunol. 3, 521 (1974)

19. Wybran, J., Fudenberg, H.: How clinically useful is T and B cell quantitation? Ann. Int. Med. 80, 765 (1974)

# Chapter 11
# Participation of Leukemia Cells in Immune Responses

M. Boranić, M. Poljak-Blaži, M. Radačić, J. Gabrilovac, and I. Hršak

## INTRODUCTION

Many tumors preserve morphological and also functional characteristics of the tissue they have originated from, e.g., they may secrete mucus, bile or milk, form bone or cartilage, grow hairs, accumulate pigment, generate action potentials, respond to hormonal stimuli, etc. This also applies to leukemia cells in that the existing classification of leukemias is based on morphological resemblances between malignant and normal cells, and that recent technical and conceptual progress permits further subclassification on the basis of the presence or absence of special markers, such as the surface immunoglobulins, receptors for antigen, Fc fragment of immunoglobulin, or complement, T-antigens, etc. (15). It has also been shown that leukemia cells share several functional properties with their normal counterparts, such as phagocytosis, chemotaxis, secretion and release of lysozyme, immunoglobulin and interferon, growth in colonies (in vivo or in vitro), and recirculation from blood to lymph (2, 7, 8, 9, 17, 18, 19, 20, 23). The ability of transfusions of leukocytes obtained from donors with chronic myeloid leukemia to combat septicemia (10) is evidently due to the fact that these cells phagocytose, respond to chemotactic stimuli, and kill bacteria by lysozyme or otherwise. It is proper to ask, therefore, whether there are other normal functions performed by leu-leukemia cells, and more specifically, do leukemia cells participate in immune responses? Our preliminary results suggested that this might be possible (3).
Here we extend these observations.

## MATERIALS AND METHODS

Mice and Leukemia. A lymphoid leukemia of A/H mice, used in these experiments, was propagated by serial transfers of cells obtained from enlarged spleens of moribund animals, and has been described earlier (2). Intravenous inoculation of $10^6$ cells kills the recipients in 9-10 days. It is very sensitive to L-asparaginase and cyclophosphamide. Numerous passages have reduced its antigenicity, yet leukemia-specific antigens can be recognized. Theta-antigen is absent (3).

In addition to A/H mice, C57Bl/6 and CBA/H mice were also used. All were produced in our colony by inbreeding.

Irradiation. This was carried out by an X-ray machine operated at 220 kV, 15 mA, 1.0 Cu, 0.5 Al, distance 42 cm, 85 R/min.

Functional Tests. Three immunological reactions were assayed in vivo: (a) response of cells injected into irradiated recipients against sheep red blood cells (SRBC), as measured by Jerne's technique (3); (b) rejection of grafts of allogeneic (C57Bl) skin (4); and (c) graft-versus-host or host-versus-graft reaction, measured by destruction of colonies of hemopoietic tissue (5).

In vitro tests included: (a) adherence of cells to glass, i.e., to walls of capillary tubes, as measured by a technique modified from that of BRYANT and SUTCLIFFE (6) and described elsewhere (21); (b) phagocytosis of bacteria Escherichia coli during 30 min. incubation at 37°C, as determined morphologically in smears stained by May-Grünwald-Giemsa; and (c) migration of cells from capillary tubes (1).

Receptors for Fc fragment of IgG, and those for complement, were tested by standard techniques.

Labeling of Cells with $^{51}$Cr. In order to follow distribution of leukemia cells in the body, they were labeled with $^{51}$Cr by incubation (in Hanks buffer) for 1 h at room temperature at a ratio of 100 μCi per $10^8$ cells. The cells were washed twice before injection.


RESULTS

Participation of Leukemia Cells in the Response to SRBC. A-strain mice, irradiated with 800 R of X-rays received cells of lymphoid leukemia, syngeneic bone marrow, syngeneic thymus, or mixtures thereof, along with the antigen, SRBC. After 8 days the animals were killed, and their spleens were assayed by Jerne's technique on the content of cells producing hemolytic antibodies (PFC). Few PFC were generated by leukemia cells given alone or mixed with bone marrow, but many PFC grew from the mixture of leukemia cells and thymocytes (Table1). Thus, leukemia cells apparently participated in the immune response. They might have generated PFC through genuine cooperation with thymus cells, or have become PFC simply by having attached (by means of surface receptors) antibodies formed by normal B-lymphocytes present in the inoculum.

Participation of Leukemia Cells in Rejection of Skin Grafts. A-strain mice injected with $10^3$ or $10^4$ cells of lymphoid leukemia received grafts of allogeneic (C57Bl) skin 1 day later. Leukemic animals rejected grafts in the same manner as the controls injected with normal cells, although the final stages of the rejection coincided with terminal stages of the disease and death. This, however, need not indicate that leukemia cells really participated in the rejection process like normal cells, because the critical events of that process - recognition of foreign tissue and initial infiltration of its bed - could have taken place at a time when the immune system of the host was still preserved, so that sloughing of the grafts proceeded to completion regardless of the advancement of leukemia. In an attempt to answer this question and see whether leukemia cells do or do not join inflammatory infiltrates underneath and within the grafts, leukemia cells labeled with $^{51}$Cr were injected into mice (5 x $10^6$ cells/mouse) that had been grafted with allogeneic skin 3 days earlier. Control animals bore grafts of syngeneic skin. Six days after injection, the grafts were excised together with their beds, to determine radioactivity. As seen in Table 2 the sites of allogeneic grafts accumulated 4 times more activity than non-graft skin, but the same was true for the sites of syngeneic grafts. It can be concluded, therefore, that leukemia cells do join inflammatory infiltrates, but cannot discriminate between those caused by immune reaction against foreign tissue and those accompanying healing in of compatible tissue.

80

Table 1. Participation of cells of lymphoid leukemia in the immune response against SRBC

| Cells injected[a] | PFC/$10^6$ injected cells |
|---|---|
| L | 750 |
| L + BM | 730 |
| L + T | 44,660 |
| BM | 300 |
| T | 0.4 |
| BM + T | 1,550 |

[a] Recipients were lethally irradiated syngeneic (A/H) mice. L = lymphoid leukemia (2.5 x $10^5$ cells), BM = bone marrow (5 x $10^6$), T = thymus (5 x $10^7$). SRBC (2 x $10^7$) were given i.v. along with cells a few hours after irradiation, and then again 4 days later (2 x $10^8$ i.p.). Recipients were killed on day 8, and spleens were processed for PFC assay. 10-30 mice per group.

Participation of Leukemia Cells in Graft-Versus-Host (GVH) and Host-Versus-Graft (HVG) Reactions. For the GVH assay, adult CBA mice were irradiated with a lethal dose of X-rays and 4 h later received 8 x $10^4$ cells of syngeneic (CBA) bone marrow mixed (1:25) with 2 x $10^6$ spleen cells of A-strain mice. These were either normal animals, or had borne leukemia for 4, 8, or 11 days. The spleens of the recipients were collected after 8 days and were examined for macroscopically visible colonies of hemopoiesis. Spleen colonies are produced both by syngeneic CFUs (from CBA bone marrow) and by allogeneic ones (from A spleens); leukemia cells do not produce colonies. Since immunocompetent cells from a spleens mount GVH reaction, CBA colonies will be destroyed, so that the colony count (depending on the severity of the GVH reaction) will approach that produced by splenic CFU alone.

For the HVG assay, lethally irradiated A mice received $10^6$ cells of allogeneic (CBA) bone marrow mixed with 25 x $10^6$ cells of A mice inoculated with leukemia or normal spleen cells 4 or 11 days previously. The spleens of the recipients were collected 4 days later, processed for histology, stained by hemalaun-eosin, and examined by microscopy for the presence of microcolonies. Microscopic instead of macroscopic colonies were counted because macroscopic colonies would have been overgrown by rapidly proliferating leukemia cells.

Table 2. Participation of leukemia cells in inflammatory reactions accompanying skin grafts

| Type of graft | Radioactivity (cpm/g)[a] (mean ± s.d.) |
|---|---|
| Allogeneic | 7200 |
| Syngeneic | 6910 |
| Non-grafted skin | 1755 |

[a] 5 x $10^6$ labeled cells per mouse were injected into animals grafted 3 days before. Grafts and their beds were excised 6 days later for measurement of radioactivity. 10 mice per group.

Table 3. Participation of leukemia cells in GVH reactions

| Cells injected[a] | Mean no. of colonies per spleen produced by mixtures of bone marrow and spleen cells obtained at various intervals after inoculation of leukemia: | | |
|---|---|---|---|
| | Day 4 | Day 8 | Day 11 |
| BM | 22.5 | 19.0 | 19.0 |
| LS | 17.0 | 18.5 | 27.0 |
| NS | 18.5 | 21.0 | 22.5 |
| BM + LS[b] | 23.5 (39.5) | 15.5 (37.5) | 28.5 (46.0) |
| BM + NS[b] | 15.5 (41.0) | 20.0 (40.0) | 27.5 (41.5) |

[a] Irradiated CBA mice received (a) syngeneic bone marrow (BM, 8 x $10^4$ cells), (b) leukemic spleen cells (LS, 2 x $10^6$) obtained from A mice inoculated with leukemia, (c) normal spleen cells (NS, 2 x $10^6$) obtained from A mice inoculated with spleen cells instead of leukemia, or (d) mixtures thereof, as indicated.

[b] In parentheses, expected numbers of colonies obtained by arithmetic summation of corresponding control values for BM, LS, or NS.

Table 4. Participation of leukemia cells in HVG reaction

| Cells injected[a] | Mean no. of colonies per spleen produced by mixtures of bone marrow and spleen cells obtained at various intervals after inoculation of leukemia | |
|---|---|---|
| | Day 4 | Day 11 |
| BM | 17.0 | 17.0 |
| LS | 10.0 | 5.0 |
| NS | 5.5 | 15.0 |
| BM + LS[b] | 10.0 (27.0) | 3.5 (22.0) |
| BM + NS[b] | 6.5 (22.5) | 11.0 (32.0) |

[a] Irradiated A mice received (a) bone marrow of allogeneic (CBA) mice (BM, $10^6$ cells); (b) leukemic spleen cells (LS, 25 x $10^6$) obtained from A mice inoculated with leukemia, (c) normal spleen cells (NS, 25 x $10^6$) obtained from A mice inoculated with spleen cells instead of leukemia, or (d) mixtures thereof, as indicated.

[b] In parenthesis, expected numbers of colonies obtained by arithmetic summation of corresponding control values for BM, LS, or NS.

As seen in Tables 3 and 4, spleen cells of mice with leukemia were as effective in reducing the colony count as the spleen cells of control mice without leukemia, regardless of the progression of the disease. This was interpreted as showing that cells of this leukemia can become recruited into the process leading to destruction of the colonies, which, like that leading to rejection of skin grafts, is probably initiated by normal immunocompetent cells present in the inoculum.

Other properties of Leukemia Cells. As seen in Tables 5 and 6, cells of this leukemia are actively phagocytic, adhere to glass, and possess surface receptors for immunoglobulin and complement, but the phagocytic activity seems to be more expressed, compared to normal cells, the adherence is somewhat weaker, and the receptor-bearing cells are less numerous.

Table 5. Phagocytic ability and adherence to glass of the cells of lymphoid leukemia

| Cells tested | Phagocytic cells (%)[a] | Adherent cells (%)[b] |
|---|---|---|
| Leukemia | 20 | 13 |
| Spleen | 23 | 45 |
| Bone marrow | 42 | 33 |
| Lymph node | 8 | 12 |

[a] Cell suspensions were incubated for 1 h at 37°C with E.coli at a ratio of 1:20. Smears were stained with May-Grünwald-Giemsa. Cells with 3 or more ingested bacteria were considered phagocytic.

[b] Cell suspensions were incubated for 20 min. at 37°C in hematocrit capillaries. Fluid contents were gently aspirated, and remaining, adherent cells were detached by EDTA in Hanks and centrifugation, and counted.

Table 6. Presence of receptors for the Fc fragment of Ig and for complement on leukemic cells

| Type of rosettes[a] | % of cells forming rosettes in the suspensions of | |
|---|---|---|
| | Leukemia cells | Normal spleen cells |
| EA | 10.8 | 19.6 |
| EAC | 11.2 | 30.7 |

[a] EA = erythrocyte-antigen complexes, for detection of Fc-receptors; EAC= erythrocyte-antigen-complement receptors, for detection of C3-receptors.

DISCUSSION

This work has shown that cells of lymphoid leukemia incompletely express several features of normal lymphoid cells, such as the presence of surface receptors for immunoglobulin and complement, adherence to glass, and participation in immune response against sheep erythrocytes and allogeneic transplantation antigens. This extends previous observations that leukemia cells share the ability of normal lymphoid cells to recognize microenvironmental compartments of the spleen, and resemble normal cells as regards distribution and recirculation in the body. However, leukemia cells migrate poorly as compared with normal spleen cells, while, on the other hand, they phagocytose more avidly than normal lymphoid cells.

Thus, like the cells of many other tumors, cells of this transplantable leukemia have preserved both the morphological and functional features of the normal cells they had originated from. Although the features are aberrant, incomplete or exaggerated, leukemia cells may, perhaps, still contribute toward immunological capacities of the organism. Since the cells lack θ-antigen but, on the other hand, adhere to glass and possess receptors for immunoglobulin, it could be assumed that they have originated from B rather than T cells and, consequently, that they participate in immune reactions in a manner which is appropriate for B-lymphocytes. This is to say that leukemia cells should be triggered into action either by mediators released from normal T cells, or by immunoglobulins which have been synthesized by normal B cells and attached onto leukemia cells or target cells.

In the reaction against SRBC, cells that acquired the ability to lyse SRBC in agar (PFC) could have been generated from leukemia cells, either through genuine cooperation of leukemia cells with normal T cells, or simply through attachment of hemolytic antibodies synthesized by normal B cells. The first possibility implies that leukemia cells have been, by chance, endowed with anti-SRBC specificity (which is improbable), or had acquired it from T cells (which is disputable; (22)). It is more likely, therefore, that leukemia cells became PFC simply by having attached anti-SRBC antibodies formed by normal B cells. Explosive multiplication of leukemia cells, "adorned" with "borrowed" antibodies, amplified the immune response beyond the limits set by proliferative ability of normal cells, thus giving the impression of false clonal growth.

In the reactions against foreign transplantation antigens, such as the rejection of skin grafts or destruction of hemopoietic tissues in graft-versus-host reaction, leukemia cells have been recruited into the inflammatory infiltrates, and apparently took an active part in destroying the targets. The lysis of target cells could be attributed to cytotoxic substances released from leukemia cells, as occurs when normal lymphocytes become activated (11, 12, 13), but it is uncertain whether leukemia cells can indeed respond in this manner (14, 16).

In conclusion, malignant alteration which has exempted leukemia cells from regulation of the growth, did not completely erase the features that are peculiar to lymphoid cells, so that the cells take part, awkwardly but still purposefully, in immune reactions of the humoral and cellular type.


SUMMARY


Cells of a transplantable lymphoid leukemia of mice were tested in vivo and in vitro to see which features of normal lymphoid cells were retained in spite of malignant transformation and lack of growth control. Leukemia cells phagocytosed, adhered to glass, possessed receptors for immunoglobulin, participated in the immune response against SRBC (probably by amplifying a normal response through attachment of antibodies on their surfaces), became recruited into inflammatory reactions elicited by grafting allogeneic or syngeneic skin, and apparently joined graft-versus-host and host-versus-graft reactions, contributing toward damage of hemopoietic target tissues.

REFERENCES

1. Boranić, M., Sabioncello, A., Radačić, M., Dekaris, D., Veselić,B.: Capillary migration of the cells of three murine tumors. Biomed. Expr. 25, 15-18 (1976)
2. Boranić, M., Dominis, M., Pavelić, Z., Blaži-Poljak, M.: Colony-forming ability of a lymphoid and a myeloid murine leukemia. J. Nat. Cancer Inst. 51, 275-282 (1973)
3. Boranić, M., Hršak, I., Marotti, T., Mažuran, R., Silobrčić, V.: "Cooperation" of normal and malignant lymphoid cells in the immune response against sheep erythrocytes. Biomed. Expr. 21, 9-12 (1974)
4. Boranić, M., Oršanić, L., Blaži, M.: Damage of the skin during acute graft-versus-host reaction in mice. Transplantation 14, 442-447 (1972)
5. Boranić, M., Toncović, I., Blaži, M.: Quantitative aspects of destruction of hemopoietic tissue in mouse radiation chimaeras. Biomed. Expr. 19, 104-107 (1973)
6. Bryant, R.E., Sutcliffe, M.C.: A method for quantitation of human leukocyte adhesion to glass. Proc. Soc. Exp. Biol. Med. 141, 196-202 (1973)
7. Constantinopoulos, A., Likhite, V., Crosby, W.H., Najjar, V.A.: Phagocytic activity of the leukemic cell and its response to the phagocytosis-stimulating tetrapeptide, tuftsin. Cancer Res. 33, 1230-1234 (1973)
8. Cooper, A.G., Brown, M.L., Derby, H.A., Wortis, H.H.: Quantitation of surface-membrane and intracellular $\gamma$, $\mu$ and $\kappa$ chains of normal and neoplastic human lymphocytes. Clin. Exp. Immunol. 13, 487-496 (1973)
9. Epstein, L.B., Cline, M.J.: Chronic lymphocytic leukemia. Studies on mitogen-stimulated lymphocyte interferon as a new technique for assessing T-lymphocyte effector function. Clin. Exp. Immunol. 16, 553-563 (1974)
10. Eyre, H.J., Goldstein, I.M., Perry, S., Graw, R.G.: Leukocyte transfusions: Function of transfused granulocytes from donors with chronic myelocytic leukemia. Blood 36, 432-442 (1970)
11. Fakhri, O., Hobbs, J.R.: Target cell death without added complement after cooperation of 7 S antibodies with non-immune lymphocytes. Nature (New Biol.) 235, 177-178 (1972)
12. Granger, G.A., Kolb, W.P.: Lymphocyte in vitro cytotoxicity: Mechanisms of immune and non-immune small lymphocyte mediated target cell destruction. J. Immunol. 101, 111-120 (1968)
13. Grant, C.K., Alexander, P.: Nonspecific cytotoxicity of spleen cells and the specific cytotoxic action of thymus-derived lymphocytes in vitro. Cell. Immunol. 14, 46-51 (1974)
14. Ling, N.R., Steel, C.M., Wallin, J., Hardy, D.A.: The interaction of normal lymphocytes from lymphoid cell lines. Immunol. 26, 345-358 (1974)
15. Mathé, G., Belpomme, D.: T and B lymphocytic nature of leukemias and lymphomas: A new and still uncertain parameter for their classification. Biomed. 20, 81-85 (1974)

16. Melief, C.J.M., Schweitzer, M., Zeylenmaker, W.P., Verhagen, E.H., Eysvogel, V.P.: Some immunological properties of lymphoid cells from patients with acute lymphatic leukemia (ALL). Clin. Exp. Immunol. 15, 131-143 (1973)

17. Meuret, G., Bundschu-Lay, A., Senn, H.J., Huhn, D.: Functional characteristics of chronic monocytic "leukemia". Acta Haematol. 52, 95-106 (1974)

18. Moore, M.A.S., Williams, N., Metcalf, D.: In vitro colony formation by normal and leukemic human hematopoietic cells: Characterization of the colony-forming cells. J. Nat. Cancer Inst. 50, 603-623 (1973)

19. Nies, K.M., Oberlin, M.A., Brown, J.C., Halpern, M.S.: Immunoglobulin biosynthesis by normal and leukemic human peripheral blood lymphocytes. J. Immunol. 111, 1236-1242 (1973)

20. Ohta, H., Matsuda, Y.: Ready release of intracellular muramidase (lysozyme) from mononuclear cells in the skin window exudates. Acta Haematol. 49, 159-165 (1973)

21. Radačić, M., Boranić, M.: Adherence of normal and leukemia cells to glass (in Croatian). Vet. Archiv (Zagreb) 45, 21-29 (1975)

22. Raff, M.C.: T and B lymphocytes and immune responses. Nature 242, 19-23 (1973)

23. Sinha, B.K., Goldenberg, H.J.: The circulation of malignant lymphoid cells in thoracic duct lymph of rats with lymphosarcoma and lymphatic leukemia. Cancer Res. 30, 2292-2296 (1970)

# Chapter 12

# Morphological Characterisation of Adult Acute Leukaemia in Short-Term Liquid Culture

F. R. BALKWILL and R. T. D. OLIVER

## INTRODUCTION

Culture of mouse (4) and human bone-marrow stem cells (8) was first reported using an agar co-culture system with a feeder layer as an exogenous source colony stimulating factor (CSF). Normal mouse marrow cells have an absolute and human marrow cells a relative dependency on CSF for growth in culture. Studies in experimental murine myeloid leukaemia established that the leukaemia cell has been able to grow in agar culture without a source of CSF, but that addition of CSF increased the number and size of colonies formed (6). In human acute myeloid leukaemia (AML) early reports failed to show colony formation in the majority of patients at the time of diagnosis, though some evidence of growth in the presence of a source of CSF was suggested by the formation of clusters and the comparison with the numbers of cells surviving for 8 days in cultures without CSF (7). Recently, using a simplified liquid culture technique, it has been possible to show that leukaemia cells from the majority of patients with acute myelogenous leukaemia are capable of growth in microculture in the absence of an extraneous source of CSF as measured by thymidine incorporation (2) (and the few cases where it was studied) actual increase in cell numbers in culture (1). In this article we report on the morphological features of the cells grown in liquid culture.

## MATERIALS AND METHODS

Patients aged from 14 to 78 years old who presented at St. Bartholomew's Hospital with acute leukaemia have been systematically studied at the time of diagnosis. Heparinised peripheral blood (10-20 ml) is first sedimented with one third of the volume of methyl cellulose at $37^{\circ}$C for 10-30 min. The supernatant **leukocytes** are removed and washed once in RPM 1640 and then adjusted to 1 x $10^6$ ml in Tc 199 and added **glutamine and asparagine with 10% foetal calf serum (Difco)**. 0.2 ml aliquots of this suspension are added to Falcon 3040 flat-bottomed microtest tissue culture plates for thymidine incorporation studies and **10 ml aliquots are added to Falcon 3013 culture flasks for morphological** studies. After 3 days culture 0.5 μci/ml tritiated for morphological to the microcultures which are harvested on a modified mash harvester for scintillation counting. At the same time the morphological characteristics are assessed in the culture flasks under phase contrast with an inverted microscope (Wild M40).

RESULTS

## Microculture Tritiated Thymidine Incorporation

Seventy patients have been studied in short-term microculture. Counts per minute incorporated varied from less than 100 up to 34,000 (Table 1). In general, though, there was no difference between the various types of myelogenous leukaemia (31 out of 48 had more than 1000 cpm/culture), the lymphatic leukaemia and lymphoma patients had significant lower incorporation (4 out of 15 with less than 1000 cpm per culture). Three out of five undifferentiated leukaemia had less than 1000 cpm per culture.

Table 1. Thymidine incorporation and acute leukaemia classification

|  | ALL and lymphoma | AUL[a] | AML | AMML |
|---|---|---|---|---|
| >10,000 | 1 | 0 | 11 | 1 |
| 500 - 10,000 | 4 | 4 | 18 | 9 |
| <500 | 11 | 1 | 8 | 0 |

AUL " Acute Undifferentiated Leukaemia.

## Culture Flask Morphology

Two extremes of morphology were apparent in the 43 cultures in falcon flasks. The majority of cultures produced two cell populations: a supernatant free-floating population ("non-stickers") and plastic/glass adherent, trypsin resistant, phagocytic population ("stickers"). A minority of the cultures produced only the free-floating population. The non-sticking cells were uniform large round cells whereas the stickers had a variable shape but were usually elongated and fusiform. On the basis of the number of stickers produced in culture it was possible to divide the cultures into five groups (see Table 2). Table 3 shows a comparison of these categories with the routine haematological diagnosis. Only one patient with acute myelo-monocytic leukaemia (AMML) failed to produce "stickers" in culture while 19 out of 43 (44%) of AML's also produced "stickers". The majority of acute lymphoid leukaemia (ALL), (AUL) and non-Hodgkin's lymphomas produced very few or no "stickers" at all. Table 4 shows the correlation between tritiated thymidine incorporation and "sticker" cell production. Although there are more "non-stickers" than "stickers" with less than 1000 cpm/culture, the patients with the three highest thymidine incorporations (21,000, 32,000 and 34,000 cpm/culture) were "non-stickers".

Table 2. Morphological classification

| +++ | = | > 50 Stickers per high power field |
|---|---|---|
| ++ | = | 20-50 Stickers per high power field |
| + | = | 5-20 Stickers per high power field |
| - ·to ± | = | < 5 Stickers per high power field |
| O | = | No growth and < 5 Stickers per high power field |

Table 3. "Sticker" cell classification
in adult acute leukaemia

|  | ALL and lymphoma | AUL | AML | AMML |
|---|---|---|---|---|
| ++ or +++ | 1 | 0 | 13 | 13 |
| 0 → + | 22 | 5 | 32 | 6 |

Table 4. Correlation of culture characteristics
and tritiated thymidine incorporation in patients
with AML

| CPM / Culture | 0 → + | ++ and +++ |
|---|---|---|
| <  1,000 | 8 | 1 |
| 1,000 - 10,000 | 17 | 10 |
| > 10,000 | 5 | 5 |

DISCUSSION

It is clear from our results that the majority of peripheral blood
cells from patients with AML have a high thymidine incorporation and
growth in short-term culture without the need for an external source
of CSF. Though there have been isolated reports of growth of monocytoid
cells from patients with myelogenous leukaemia (9), there have been no
previous detailed morphological study of such a large series. Of particular interest is the finding that in 44% of patients, the AML as opposed
to AMML produces these "sticker" cells. These findings are supported by
the recent electron microscopy studies of GLICK and HORN (5) who demonstrated promonocytes and monocytes in 18 out of 25 cases of non-lymphoid
acute leukaemia which they studied, though standard light microscopic
examination had not detected them. So far electron micrographic and
cytochemical studies as well as phagocytic assays of the sticker cells
in our cultures (6) have not been able to differentiate the sticker
cells from normal macrophages. However, autoradiographs have shown some
heavily labelled cells which do not occur with normal macrophages in
culture, though they are seen with activated macrophages. Clearly it is
likely that these monocytic cells are a result of the malignant proliferation. However, it will be important to exclude the possibility that
these cells are part of the host response to the leukaemia as it is
well-recognised that a high macrophage content of experimental tumours
is associated with a relatively slower rate of growth and lower incidence of metastases. GAVCI et al. (4a) have found host histocompata-
bility antigens on the plastic adherent cells in a rat myelogenous
leukaemia arising in the 1 August strain that had been passaged in
an August x Marshall F1 host. Preliminary analysis of the patients
reported in this study (BALKWILL and OLIVER (1)) suggest that there is
a better prognosis in terms of incidence of complete remission and
survival time in those patients who produced "sticker" cells in culture.

Our findings in patients with ALL and non-Hodgkin's lymphoma is not surprising as even in the agar colony system no one has reported growth of lymphoid cells from bone marrow of normal individuals or patients with lymphatic leukaemia. Clearly, other factors than CSF, such as thymic hymoral factors (10) or ubiquitous immunopoietic protein (3), are required.

SUMMARY

Peripheral blood leukocytes from 31 out of 48 patients with acute myelogenous leukemia grew in short-term liquid culture. Two distinct types of growth occurred. The first type was dimorphic with supernatant free-floating ("non-sticker") cells and, in addition, a plastic/glass adherent, trypsin resistant, phagocytic population ("stickers"). The second type which occurred less frequently than the first consisted almost entirely of free-floating "non-sticker" cells. Although patients with this second type of growth pattern almost invariably had AML, 44% of AML's produced monocytoid "sticker" cells in culture. Cells from the majority of patients with ALL did not grow in culture.

REFERENCES

1. Balkwill, F.R., Oliver, R.T.D.: Diagnostic and Prognostic Significance of Peripheral Blood Central Characteristics in Adult Leukaemia. Brit. J. of Cancer, 33, 400-410 (1976)
1a. Balkwill, F.R., Oliver, R.T.D., Crowther, D.: The Investigation of Host Factors Influencing the Growth of Leukaemia Cells using a New Liquid Microculture Technique. Proceedings of a Meeting on Clinical Application of Short-Term Cultures of Human Tumour Biopsy Specimens. In: Human Tumours in Short Term Culture, Techniques and Applications (ed. P.P. Dendy). New York: Academic Press 1976
2. Balkwill, F., Pindar, A., Crowther, D.: Factors influencing microculture of leukaemia cells. Nature 251, No. 5477, 741 (1974)
3. Boyse, E.A., Abbott,J.: Surface reorganisation as an initial inductive event in the differentiation. of prothymocytes to thymocytes. Fed. Proc. 34, No. 1, 24-27 (1975)
4. Bradley, T.R., Metcalf, D.: The growth of mouse bone marrow cells in vitro. Austral. exp. Biol. Med. Sci. 44, 287 (1966)
4a. Gavci, Ch., Wrathmell, A., Alexander, P.: The Origin and Role of Blood Borne Monocytes in Rats with a Transplantable Acute Myelogenous Leukaemia. Cancer Letters 1, 33 (1975)
5. Glick, A.D., Horn, R.G.: Identification of promonocytes and monocytoid precursors in acute leukaemia od adults: ultrastructural and cytochemical observations. Brit. Haematol. 26, 395 (1974)
6. Metcalf, D., Moore, M.A.S., Warner, N.L.: Colony formation in vitro by myelomonocytic leukaemic cells. Nat. Cancer Inst. 43, 983 (1969)
7. Moore, M.A.S., Williams, N., Metcalf, D.: In vitro colony formation by normal and leukaemic human haematopoietic cells: Characterisation of the colony-forming cells. Nat. Cancer Inst. 50, 603 (1973)
8. Pike, B.L., Robinson, W.A.: Human bone marrow colony growth in vitro. Cell. Physiol. 76, 77 (1970)
9. Schmalzl, F., Braunsteiner, H.: II. On the origin of monocytes. Acta. Haematol. 39, 177 (1968)
10. Trainin, N.: Thymic hormones and the immune response. Physiol. Rev., in Press (1973)

# Chapter 13

# Surface Cell Markers in Human Lymphoid Malignancies *

M. Seligmann, J. L. Preud'homme, and J. C. Brouet

Surface markers considered to be specific for human thymus-derived (T)
or bone-marrow-derived (B) cells have provided new insights into the
pathogenesis of several lymphoid malignancies. This study as well as
that of leukaemia-associated membrane antigens will probably enable
hematologists to achieve new classifications of some leukemias and
lymphomas which will not be merely based upon morphologic criteria and
which will thus become more accurate and reproducible.

## 1. CRITICAL EVALUATION OF THE METHODS

Although most techniques used for identification of B and T cells are
relatively well standardized (2), the diagnostic value of these markers needs critical evaluation. The interpretation of the results of
such investigations requires great caution, since they are exposed to
a number of pitfalls. Membrane-bound immunoglobulins (Ig) detectable
by immunofluorescence constitute the most reliable marker of B cells
and represent a clonal marker of B-cell proliferations when monospecific
antiserums to the various immunoglobulin chains are used. But the mere
presence of immunoglobulins at the surface of a cell does not necessarily mean that they are produced by that cell (30). Erroneous interpretations may result from: the attachment of circulating immune complexes or IgG aggregates to any cell carrying receptors for C3/or Fc;
an anti-IgG (rheumatoid factor) activity of membrane-bound IgM; or
the presence of antibodies to surface determinants on B- or T-lymphocytes. In leukemic disorders, antibodies may be directed toward "neoplastic" surface antigens. In vitro experiments may therefore be required to ensure that surface immunoglobulins are synthetized by the
cells under study. Receptors for C3/and for the Fc fragment of IgG
are commonly used as markers of B-lymphocytes. However, some B-lymphocytes lack the C3/receptors and, although most B lymphocytes bind aggregated human IgG, other techniques used to identify the receptors
for the Fc fragment of IgG may yield quite different results. Fc receptors are also present on a subset of (activated?) T-lymphocytes.

The membranes of monocytes also bear receptors for complement and may
bind IgG from human or animal serum. This is a major source of potential errors of interpretation. Unidentified lymphocyte-like cells which
bear C3/and Fc receptors without producing membrane-bound Ig may well
belong to the monocytic series.

* Supported in part by grants from D.G.S.T. No. 74.7.0607., and I.N.S.
E.R.M. (ATP 16) No. 73.16.17 and (ATP 31) No. 10.74.31.3.

Most hetero-antisera to B or T cells are only relatively specific.
When they can be used only in cytotoxicity tests and not in immunofluorescence, they do not allow direct checking for other markers and
direct examination of the positive cells.

Current studies have shown that the delineation between B- and T-lymphocyte markers is less clearcut than previously appraised and that
cell subpopulations are of utmost importance within these two broad
categories. It should be stressed that a classification of cells in
terms of B or T origin,even if appearing relatively safe for normal
lymphocytes may not be valid when extrapolated to undifferentiated or
neoplastic cells. Such cells may express membrane antigens only at
certain stages of the cell cycle or experience surface changes which
could prevent their identification. Moreover, leukemic cells acquire
new antigenic determinants which may invalidate results obtained with
antisera raised to B or T fetal or neoplastic cells. The need for
using several membrane markers in the study of leukemias amd lymphomas
is clearly obvious. Despite these limitations and pitfalls, B- and T-
cell markers have provided new approches and concepts in the study of
lymphoproliferative diseases (34).


2. MONOCLONAL B-CELL PROLIFERATIONS


Most lymphoid malignancies featured by a B-cell proliferation appear
to be of monoclonal origin, as outlined by the study of membrane-bound
Ig which constitute a clonal marker. Although the immunofluorescent
staining of fresh cells from patients with chronic lymphoid leukemia
(CLL) (the vast majority being B-cell leukemias) or other B-cell malignancies, may reveal more than one kind of surface Ig and lead to
a false polyclonal appearance, surface Ig synthesis in vitro was shown
to be restricted to a single light chain type and to μ, γ, or α heavy
chains, the actual cell product belonging most often to the IgM class
(29). In IgG-producing CLL cells, restriction with regard to IgG subclass and allotypes was demonstrated (17). The finding in several
cases of CLL of the same idiotypic specificity (18, 33) or of the same
defined antibody activity (15, 19, 27, 29) of the surface Ig on all proliferating lymphocytes reflects identical variable regions of the surface Ig and further substantiates the monoclonal nature of the disease.
This conclusion is not invalidated by the recent finding of the simul-
taneous presence of ∂- and μ-chains on the proliferating B cells from
many patients (19, 24, 31). In fact, most μ-chain-bearing lymphocytes
from normal blood also express and synthesize ∂-chains and IgD and
IgM molecules on the same cell or proliferating clone have identical
light chains, and share identical idiotypic specificity and eventually
antibody activity (18, 26, 33). Both molecules differ therefore only in
the constant part of their heavy chains. Despite the usual absence of increase in blood lymphocyte counts, a high percentage of the circulating
lymphocytes in untreated patients with Waldenström's macroglobulinemia
exhibit a surface monoclonal IgM and belong therefore to the proliferating clone (28). Surface Ig studies in CLL also allowed the detection of biclonal processes (29). In some cases the two clones seemed
unrelated whereas in other instances they may have a common origin.

Another concept brought forward by the study of membrane cell markers
is that monoclonal B-cell proliferations vary considerably with respect to the type(s) of proliferating cells and their level within the
normal pathway of differentiation of a B-cell clone (32). In some pleo-
morphic lymphoid cell neoplasms such as Waldenström's macroglobulinemia,
the proliferating B cells can still undergo differentiation and

uninterrupted maturation from the small lymphocyte to the IgM-secreting plasma cell (28). In other B-cell malignancies, the proliferating cells appear to be "frozen" at a given point along the pathway of differentiation. The leukemic lymphocytes in most cases of CLL seem unable to mature further, and a uniform pattern of the surface Ig on all the proliferating lymphocytes of a given patient accords with the hypothesis that their development was arrested at the same stage (29). However, in some patients the block in maturation is incomplete and some of the cells of the proliferating clone do mature into plasma cells which secrete in the serum a detectable monoclonal component identical to that of the lymphocytic membrane-bound Ig (26, 29). Such cases should be considered as intermediate between common CLL and macroglobulinemia featured by persistent maturation of the neoplastic clone. In some B-cell lymphomas, such as most "lymphoblastic" sarcomas and some "reticulum cell" sarcomas (7, 21), the large malignant cells may represent triggered B-lymphocytes unable to differentiate further. Since these cells, heavily loaded with surface Ig, seem to be frozen at a point located further than the small lymphocyte along the pathway of B-cell differentiation, the term "poorly differentiated" which has been used for many years appear to a misnomer.

A new and more severe type of proliferation may occur in some patients previously affected with lymphoid B-cell malignancies such as CLL and macroglobulinemia. Two examples of this situation are the rare acute blastic transformation of CLL and the so-called reticulum histiocytic lymphomas supervening on CLL or macroglobulinemia. In both instances, the new type of cells were shown to synthesize the same Ig chain as the previous lymphoid proliferation, thus ascertaining that the two cell populations derived from the same B clone (7, 8).

Investigations of membrane markers in rare proliferative diseases may lead to the individualization of minor subsets of normal lymphoid cells. Thus the "hairy cells" of tricholeukocytic leukemia (leukemic reticuloendotheliosis), the study of which has led to controversial interpretations, appear to represent peculiar Ig-producing phagocytic cells with an as yet undefined normal counterpart.


3. T-CELL PROLIFERATION


Since the initial description by SEZARY and BOUVRAIN of large abnormal circulating cells in some patients with erythrodermia, the origin of the so-called Sezary cells has much been disputed. Sezary cells, whether large or small, were shown to lack B-cell markers and to form E rosettes and were killed by hetero-antisera to T-cells, indicating their T-lymphocyte-derived nature (4, 6). It is noteworthy, that the immunological studies of the mycosis fungoides cells also point to their likely T-cell origin, thus leading to a unified concept of some cutaneous lymphoma (36).

Chronic lymphocytic leukemia of T-cell origin appeared at first to be a very rare disorder. A recent study of 11 such patients in our laboratory (5, 10) suggests that this assumption was incorrect. Nine of the 11 patients presented with unusual clinical and hematological features. The most frequent abnormalities were a considerable spleen enlargement, a moderate blood and bone-marrow invasion, the presence of cytoplasmic granules and a high content of lysosomal enzymes in the proliferating lymphocytes. This peculiar presentation was so striking that T-derived CLL was considered probable before any immunological study in the most recent patients was made. The reactivity of the

leukemic cells with several hetero-antisera varied greatly from patient to patient, suggesting that in a given patient the proliferating
cells arose from only one subset of T-lymphocytes.


4. ACUTE LYMPHOBLASTIC LEUKEMIAS


The study of membrane cell markers in acute leukemias allows one to
attempt an immunological classification of this group of diseases.
Those patients with a monoclonal B-cell proliferation are usually not
affected with common acute lymphoblastic leukemia (ALL). These B-cell
acute leukemias belong mostly to two specific entities characterized
by unusual clinical or cytological features. In three cases as described above, the blastic proliferation supervened in patients previously affected with common CLL (8). In eight cases, the blast cells
possessed all the cytological features of Burkitt's tumor cells.
Since the leukemic presentation of this disease is distinctly unusual,
the finding in all patients of a monoclonal B-cell proliferation supports the view that these peculiar ALL are closely linked to Burkitt's
lymphoma (16). Only three patients with a monoclonal B-cell process
belonged to our group of a hundred unselected patients with common
ALL. In two of these patients, the blast cells had unusual cytological
features suggestive of poorly differentiated lymphocytic lymphoma.
These findings suggest that most if not all cases of B-derived "ALL"
may in fact correspond to lymphomas with a leukemic presentation. Within common ALL, two main groups are found. In 30% of the patients, the
blast cells have T-cell-surface features (3, 12, 23). High white-blood-
cell count, tumoral disease, thymic enlargement, and strong acid phosphatase activity of the blast cells are more frequent in patients with
T-derived ALL (13, 14, 35). The largest group is characterized by the
absence of detectable B or T markers and by the presence of at least
two kinds of leukemia-associated antigens, which allow this subgroup
of ALL to be clearly delineated since T-derived ALL cells do not possess these antigens (10, 13, 20). This proposed classification dividing
ALL into three groups appears to be valid and there is some hope that
it will not remain purely academic. The elucidation of the origin of
the leukemic cells may prove to be of practical value and to have
therapeutic and prognostic implications.


5. NON-HODGKIN'S LYMPHOMAS


Most non-Hodgkin's lymphomas are monoclonal B-cell malignancies (7,
1, 21, 25). This applies to well-differentiated lymphocytic lymphoma,
closely related to CLL, and to most cases of poorly differentiated
lymphocytic lymphoma in adults. However a few cases of T-cell origin
were observed. This latter situation seems more frequent in children
(22). It should be noted that these childhood T-lymphomas appear in
many respects to be related to T-derived ALL. The main interest of
the results obtained in mixed "lymphocytic-histiocytic" lymphomas
was to demonstrate that the morphologically different cells invading
the lymph nodes usually all carry the same markers.

The present evaluation of "histiocytic" lymphomas is more confusing
(9). A B-cell origin was documented in only a few cases and it must
be stressed that, in our experience, such B-type "histiocytic" lymphomas arose in patients previously affected with well-documented B-cell
neoplasia. In a few instances the surface characteristics of the cells

were suggestive of a T-lymphocytic or histiocytic origin. In most cases the abnormal cells lacked T- or B-membrane markers. This negative finding does not of course rule out their possible lymphoid origin. The so-called histiocytic lymphomas therefore surely correspond to a heterogeneous group of diseases.

REFERENCES

1. Aisenberg, A.C., Long, J.C.: Lymphocyte surface characteristics in malignant lymphoma. Amer. J. Med. 58, 300 (1975)
2. Aiuti, F., Cerottini, J.C., Coombs, R.R.A., Cooper, M., Dickler, H.B., Fröland, S., Fudenberg, H.H., Greaves, M.F., Grey, H.M., Kunkel, H.G., Natvig, J., Preud'homme, J.L., Rabellino, E., Rowe, D.S., Seligmann, M., Siegal, F.P., Stjernsward, J., Terry, W.D., Wybran, J.: Identification, enumeration and isolation of B and T lymphocytes from human peripheral blood. Report of a WHO sponsored workshop on human B and T cells. Scand. J. Immunol. 3, 521 (1974) and in Clin. Immunol. Immunopath. 3, 584 (1975)
3. Belpomme, D., Dautcher, D., Du Rusquec, E., Grandjon, D., Huchet, R., Pouillart, P., Schwarzenberg, L., Amiel, J.L., Mathe, G.: Marqueurs des lymphocytes B et T sur les cellules neoplastiques de 20 malades atteints de leucémie lymphoide aigue et 10 atteints de leucémie lymphoide chronique. Biomed. 20, 109 (1974)
4. Broome, J.D., Zucker-Franklin, D., Weiner, M.S., Bianco, S., Nussenzweig, V.: Leukemic cells with membrane properties of thymus derived (T) lymphocytes in a case of Sezary's syndrome: morphologic and immunologic studies. Clin. Immunol. Immunopath. 1, 319 (1973)
5. Brouet, J.C., Flandrin, G., Sasportes, M., Preud'homme, J.L., Seligmann, M.: Chronic lymhocytic leukemia of T cell origin. An immunological and clinical evaluation in eleven patients. Lancet, ii, 890 (1975)
6. Brouet, J.C., Flandrin, G., Seligmann, M.: Indications for the thymus derived nature of the proliferating cells in six patients with Sezary's syndrome. New Eng. J. Med. 289, 341 (1973)
7. Brouet, J.C., Labaume, S., Seligmann, M.: Evaluation of T and B lymphocyte membrane markers in human non-Hodgkin malignant lymphomas. Brit. J. Cancer 31, suppl. II, 121 (1975)
8. Brouet, J.C., Preud'homme, J.L., Seligmann, M., Bernard, J.: Blast cells with monoclonal surface immunoglobutin in two cases of acute blast crisis supervening on chronic lymphocytic leukaemia. Brit. Med. J. 4, 23 (1973)
9. Brouet, J.C., Preud'homme, J.L., Flandrin, G., Chelloul, N., Seligmann, M.: Membrane markers in so-called "histiocytic" lymphomas, J. Nat. Canc. Inst. 56, 631 (1976)
10. Brouet, J.C., Preud'homme, J.L., Seligmann, M.: The use of B and T membrane markers in the classification of human leukemias, with special reference to acute lymphoblastic leukemia. Blood Cells, 1, 81 (1975)
11. Brouet, J.C., Prieur, A.M.: Membrane markers on chronic lymhocytic leukemia cells: a B cell leukemia with rosettes due to anti-sheep erythrocytes antibody activity of the membrane bound IgM and a T cell leukemia with surface ig. Clin. Immunol. Immunopath. 2, 481 (1974)
12. Brouet, J.C., Tosen, H.R., Chevalier, A., Seligmann, M.: T and B membrane markers on blast cells in 69 patients with acute lymphoblastic leukemia. Ann. Immunol. (Paris) 125 C, 691 (1974)

13. Brouet, J.C., Valensi, F., Daniel, M.T., Flandrin, G., Preud'homme, J.L., Seligmann, M.: Immunological classification of acute lymphoblastic leukemias. Evaluation of its clinical significance. Brit. J. Haemat., _33_, 157 (1976)

14. Catovsky, D., Goldman, J.M., Okos, A., Frisch, B., Galton, D.A.G.: T lymphoblastic leukemia: a distinct variant of acute leukemia. Brit. Med. J. _II_, 643 (1974)

15. Feizi, T., Wernet, P., Kunkel, H.G., Douglas, S.D.: Lymphocytes forming red cell rosettes in the cold in patients with chronic cold agglutinin disease. Blood _42_, 753 (1973)

16. Flandrin, G., Brouet, J.C., Daniel, M.T., Preud'homme, J.L.: Acute leukemia with Burkitt's tumor cells. A study of six cases with special reference to lymphocyte surface markers. Blood _45_, 183 (1975)

17. Fröland, S.S., Natvig, J.B.: Class, subclass and allelic exclusion od membrane-bound Ig of human B lymphocytes. J. Exp. Med. _136_, 409 (1972)

18. Fu, S.M., Winchester, R.J., Feizi, T., Walzer, P.D., Kunkel, H.G.: Idiotypic specificity of surface immunoglobulin and the maturation of leukemic bone-marrow-derived lymphocytes. Proc. Nat. Acad. Sci. USA _71_, 4487 (1974)

19. Fu, S.M., Winchester, R.J., Kunkel, H.G.: Occurrence of surface IgM, IgD and free light chains on human lymphocytes. J. Exp. Med. _139_, 451 (1974)

20. Greaves, F.M., Brown, G., Rapson, N.T., Lister, T.A.: Antisera to acute lymphoblastic leukemia cells. Clin. Immunol. Immunopath. _4_, 67 (1975)

21. Jaffe, E.S., Shevach, E.M., Sussman, E.H., Frank, M., Green, I., Berard, C.W.: Membrane receptor sites for the identification of lymphoreticular cells in benign and malignant conditions. Brit. J. Cancer _31_, suppl. II, 107 (1975)

22. Kaplan, J., Mastrangelo, R., Peterson, W.D.: Childhood lymphoblastic lymphoma, a cancer of thymus-derived lymphocytes. Cancer Res. _34_, 521 (1974)

23. Kersey, J.H., Sabad, A., Gajl-Peczalska, K.J., Halgreen, H.M., Yunis, E.J., Nesbit, M.E.: Acute lymphoblastic leukemia cells with T (thymus-derived) lymphocyte markers. Science _182_, 1355 (1973)

24. Kubo, R.T., Grey, H.M., Pirofsky, B.: IgD: a major immunoglobulin on the surface of lymphocytes from patients with chronic lymphatic leukemia. J. Immunol. _112_, 1952 (1974)

25. Leech, J.H., Glick, A.D., Waldron, J.A., Flexner, J.M., Horn, R.G., Collins, R.D.: Malignant lymphomas of follicular center cell origin in man. J. Nat. Cancer Inst. _54_, 11 (1975)

26. Pernis, S., Brouet, J.C., Seligmann, M.: IgD and IgM on the membrane of lymphoid cells in macroglobulinemia. Evidence for identity of membrane IgD and IgM antibody activity in a case with anti-IgG receptors. Europ. J. Immunol. _4_, 776 (1974)

27. Preud'homme, J.L., Seligmann, M.: Anti-human IgG activity of membrane-bound monoclonal immunoglobulin M in lymphoproliferative disorders Proc. Nat. Acad. Sci. USA _69_, 2132 (1972)

28. Preud'homme, J.L., Seligmann, M.: Immunoglobulins on the surface of lymphoid cells in Waldenström's macroglobulinemia. J. Clin. Invest. _51_, 701 (1972)

29. Preud'homme, J.L., Seligmann, M.: Surface-bound immunoglobulins as a cell marker in human lymphoproliferative diseases. Blood _40_, 777 (1972)

30. Preud'homme, J.L., Seligmann, M.: Surface immunoglobulins on human lymphoid cells. Progr. Clin. Immunol. _2_, 121 (1974)

31. Preud'homme, J.L., Brouet, J.C., Clauvel, J.P., Seligmann, M.: Surface IgD immunoproliferative disorders. Scand. J. Immunol. _3_, 853 (1974)

32. Salmon, S.E., Seligmann, M.: B-cell neoplasia in man. Lancet ii, 1230 (1974)
33. Salsano, F., Fröland, S.S., Natvig, J.B., Michaelsen, T.E.: Same idiotype of B-lymphocyte membrane IgD and IgM. Formal evidence for monoclonality of chronic lymphocytic leukemia cells. Scand. J. Immunol. 3, 841 (1974)
34. Seligmann, M., Preud'homme, J.L., Brouet, J.C.: B and T cell markers in human proliferative blood diseases and primary immunodeficiencies, with special reference to membrane bound immunoglobulins. Transpl. Rev. 16, 85 (1973)
35. Sen, L., Borella, L.: Clinical importance of lymphoblasts with T markers in childhood acute leukemia. New Eng. J. Med. 292, 828 (1975)
36. Zucker-Franklin, D., Melton, J.W., Quagliata, F.: Ultrastructural, immunologic and functional studies on Sezary cells: a neoplastic variant of thymus derived (T) lymphocytes. Proc. Nat. Acad. Sci. 71, 1877 (1974)

# Chapter 14

# An Immunological Classification of Leukemias and Hematosarcomas Based on Cell Membrane Markers with Special Reference to Null Cell Disorders

D. Belpomme, N. Lelarge, F. Feuilhade de Chauvin, R. Joseph, and G. Mathé

The identification, several years ago, of membrane markers on the mono-nuclear cell population of both animals (29) and humans (2, 10, 16, 19, 35, 38, 39, 40) has permitted differentiation of this population into T- (thymodependent) and B- (thymoindependent) lymphocytes and a third cell category including monocytes (11, 18).

The presence of these markers on normal as well as neoplastic cells of lymphomonocytoid proliferative disorders has led to efforts to re-classify human hematological diseases into different immunological categories (2, 3, 4, 23, 38).

How these new classifications are clinically useful still remains un-certain, but it is evident from these studies that new concepts con-cerning the mechanism of cancerogenesis and the origin of these neo-plastic cell proliferations have emerged (2, 3, 23, 37).

In previous papers we have shown that acute lymphoid leukemia (ALL) is a T-cell disorder in 25% of the cases, while chronic lymphoid leu-kemia (CLL) is a B-cell disorder in 90% (2, 3, 4).

We have shown, in addition, that while non-Hodgkin's hematosarcomas are B-cell diseases in the majority of cases, they are of the T type in some of them (4, 6, 7).

We have, in fact, emphasized that by using these markers in ALL, as well as in non-Hodgkin's hematosarcomas, there were neoplasia which could not be typed as T or B, and that this proliferation may be re-lated to so-called null cell disorders (2, 3, 4).

These findings, however, need critical evaluation since: (a) techni-cal problems are still encountered in the detection of lymphocyte membrane markers, and (b) results published in the literature dealing with so-called null cell disorders most often concern a limited series of cases (20, 29).

The purpose of our investigations was firstly, to assess the value of the immunological methods available for the characterization of nor-mal human mononuclear cells and, secondly, to report our findings, based on these techniques in an attempt to classify 150 cases of mono-nuclear cell proliferative disorders. This study will evaluate the frequency of so-called null cell diseases, and will give a clinical summary of these cases.

METHOD AND MATERIAL

1. Immunological Methods

Table 1 shows different membrane markers and the tests used to characterize T- and B-lymphocytes and monocytes. Table 2 presents the membrane phenotypes of the different normal human mononuclear cells.

Details of the test procedures used have already been reported (2).

Table 1. Cell membrane markers for normal lymphocytes and monocytes
in humans

| Marker | Test | T | B | Third category[a] |
|---|---|---|---|---|
| SRBC receptors | E rosettes | + | O | O |
| MRBC receptors | E rosettes | O | + | O |
| Fc ag-IgG receptors | EA rosettes | (+) (?) | (+) (?) | (+) |
| Fc Ig receptors | Immunofluores- cence with heat aggregated Ig | O | + | + (?) |
| Activated $C_3$ (d or b) receptors | EAC rosettes | O | (+) | (+) |
| Membrane Ig | Membrane immu- nofluorescence | O | + | O |
| Specific T, or B hetero antigen(s) | Cytotoxicity or immunofluo- rescence | +,O | O,+ | O,O |
| EBV receptors | Rosettes | O | (+) | O |

| | |
|---|---|
| RBC | : Sheep red blood cell. |
| MRBC | : Murine red blood cell. |
| Fc ag-IgG | : Fc receptors for antigen-IgG antibody complexes |
| Fc-Ig | : Fc receptors for immunoglobulins |
| Activated $C_3'$ | : Activated $C_3'$ complement receptors |
| EBV receptors | : Receptors for Epstein-Barr virus |
| E rosettes | : Spontaneous rosettes |
| EA rosettes | : Binding of erythrocytes sensitized with anti-erythro- cyte antibodies |
| EAC rosettes | : Binding of erythrocytes sensitized with anti-erythro- cyte antibodies |

[a] Non-T non-B mononuclear cells including monocytes.

( ) On some cells

Table 2. Membrane phenotypes of human T- and B-lymphocytes and monocytes

| | | | | | | | | | | | |
|---|---|---|---|---|---|---|---|---|---|---|---|
| T cell | = | mIg (-), | Fc,agIg$^a$ (-), | Fc (-), | $C_3$ (-), | | | E (+), | Em (-) | T ag (+) | B ag (-) |
| B cell | = | mIg (+), | Fc,agIg (+), | Fc (+), | $C_3b$ (+), | $C_3d^b$ (+), | | E (-), | Em (+), | T ag (-), | B ag (+) |
| "Monocyte" | = | mIg (-), | Fc,agIg (+), | Fc (-), | $C_3b$ (+), | $C_3d^b$ (+), | | E (-), | Em (?), | T ag (-), | B ag (-) |

mIg      Membrane immunoglobulins

FcagIg   Fc receptors for antigen Ig antibody complexes

Fc       Fc "receptors" for free immunoglobulins

$C_3'$   Activated $C_3'$ complement receptors; two subvarieties $C_3'b$ and $C_3'd$ (see text)

E        Spontaneous rosette formation with SRBC (see Table 1)

Em       Spontaneous rosette formation with MRBC (see Table 1)

Tag      Specific T heteroantigen(s)

Bag      Specific B heteroantigen(s)

$^a$ Present on educated T cells (?); possible characteristics of K cells (?).

$^b$ Involved in the immune adherence phenomenon.

Table 3. T- and B-cell markers in normal peripheral blood, bone marrow, and thymus

| | Rosettes (%)[a] | | | | | | mIg[a] (%) | |
|---|---|---|---|---|---|---|---|---|
| | E | | EA | | EAC | | | |
| Peripheral blood (50 normal subjects) | 50[b] | 25-80[c] | 10 | 5-15 | 15 | 5-25 | 23 | 10-40 |
| Bone marrow (3 normal subjects) | 22 | 16-28 | 9 | 5-14 | 44 | 36-53 | 30 | |
| Thymus (6 normal subjects) | 97 | 83-100 | ND | ND | ND | ND | 3 | 2-5 |

[a] See Tables 1 and 2 for abbreviations. Results are expressed as the ratio of total number of positve cells on total number on mononuclear cells cells.

[b] Mean value.

[c] Range.

[d] Increased mean value are now obtained in our laboratory by using a sensitized test (see JOSEPH 1976a, 1976b).

Table 3 gives the values obtained by these techniques for mononuclear cells from the peripheral blood, bone marrow, and thymus of 50 normal subjects used as controls. This data concurs with that published in the report of a WHO/IARC sponsored workshop (1974).

Although most of the techniques described here are now well-standardized, the practice of these tests, as well as the interpretation of the results, needs critical evaluation. From Table 4 it can be seen that there are some difficulties:

1. The formation of spontaneous E rosettes (E-rosette test) with sheep red blood cells (SRBC) requires special attention since a minor technical modification may induce major variations in the results. From Figure 1 it can be seen that there are at least four variable parameters involved in the test (4).

2. The detection of membrane immunoglobulins (mIg), should not be confused with the evidence of surface immunoglobulins (sIg). Only the former seems to be specific for B-lymphocytes, since the latter (sIg) may be: (a) free immunoglobulins (Ig) (including antibodies) (4), or (b) aggregated Ig (15), coating the membrane of various cells, (c) serum immune antigen-antibody complexes adhering to Fc receptors of monocytes (18), B-lymphocytes (2, 3), (activated?) T-lymphocytes (34) or K cells (28) as well as to activated $C_3$ receptors of monocytes (18) or B-lymphocytes (9, 35).

These various possibilities make the direct immunofluorescence test for mIg difficult to interpret and require proof that mIg are, in fact, synthetized by the B-lymphocytes (38).

Table 4. Critical evaluation of the test procedures for detecting membrane markers

| | |
|---|---|
| E-rosette tests | Variablility of the test (differing techniques and results according to authors). |
| EA-rosette tests | EA receptors may be detected on some educated T-lymphocytes, on some B cells, as well as on monocytes and K cells |
| EAC-rosette tests | No good control distinguishing EA from EAC receptors |
| Membrane immunofluorescence | Difficult to obtain specific antisera. Membrane Ig have to be distinguishable from surface Ig. Ig monoclonicity is required for neoplastic B lymphoid cells. |
| Specific anti T or B heterosera | Difficult to obtain truly specific hetero antisera. Immunofluorescence tests are not specific. Cytotoxicity tests do not allow correlation with morphological studies. |
| EBV membrane receptors | Difficulty due to the quality of the EBV + permanent cell line used in the test. |

For abbreviations see Tables 1 and 2; for references, see text.

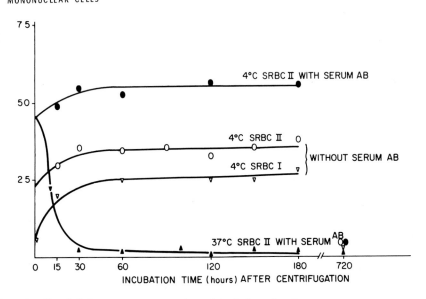

Fig. 1. *Variable parameters involved in the E-rosette-test procedure. Experimental data concern the peripheral blood of six normal adult subjects. Note that the temperature, the quantity of SRBC, the incubation time, and the eventual addition of human serum, which had been heat decomplemented and absorbed with SRBC, have to be considered*

3. Other difficulties concern the application of the immunological techniques used for normal circulating cells to neoplastic solid tissues: (a) there is a loss of cells during purification of mono-nuclear elements and thus possibly a cell selection; (b) presence of both normal and neoplastic cells in tumor tissues requires systematic morphological control to verify which cell possess the markers.
4. Finally data on cell-membrane typing using immunological criteria have to be correlated with other diagnostic methods such as the clinical picture, cytology, histology, and conventional and scanning electron microscopy (13). These general considerations stress the need for the use of a battery of tests, rather than any single one, when applying these techniques in the classification of hematological neoplastic disorders.

## 2. Diagnostic Criteria

All the disorders described here have been classified according to the criteria recommended by the W.H.O. classification of leukemias and hematosarcomas (26), and all the material has been studied in patients in an perceptible phase of their disease.

Pathological cells from the peripheral blood and/or the bone marrow of 132 patients with malignant hematological disorders have been investigated. These cases include: chronic lymphoid leukemia (CLL): 45 cases; typical primary acute lymphoid leukemia (typical primary ALL): 30 cases; typical acute myeloid leukemia (AML): 19 cases; leukemic lymphosarcoma (LLS): 15 cases; blastic crisis of chronic myeloid leukemia (CML): 6 cases; primary immunoblastic acute lymphoid leukemia (primary IALL): 4 cases; hairy cell leukemia (HCL): 4 cases; myeloma: 3 cases; primary macroglobulinemia: 2 cases; acute monocytoid leukemia (AMoL): 2 cases; chronic proplasmocytic leukemia (with macroglobu-linemia) (CPL): 1 case; chronic monocytoid leukemia (CMoL): 1 case.

In addition, pathological cells from lymph-node biopsies of 18 patients with non-Hodgkin's hematosarcomas, including 16 nonleukemic lympho-sarcomas (nonleukemic LS) and two reticulosarcomas (RS) have been studied.

## RESULTS

### 1. General Categorization

Table 5 presents the four different membrane phenotypes which were encountered in this study, when the diseases were classified according to immunological markers: 10.6% of the cases studies (16/150) were typed as T (Group I), 44% (67/150) as B (Group II), while 40% of cases (61/150) were found to have cells with no detectable membrane markers in the technical conditions used (Group III), and 4% (6/150) to have cells bearing activated complement and/or Fc receptors, which make these disorders difficult to identify (Group IV).

### 2. Analysis of the Different Disorders According to the Four Immuno-logical Groups

#### 2.1. T-cell Neoplasia (Group I)
Table 6 summarizes our results: 50% of cases (8/16) of T-cell disorders are devoted to primary ALL, while 50% of the remaining cases

include fice cases of LS, two cases of CLL, and one case of blastic crisis of CML.

From this data, it is confirmed that in ALL, one case out of four is classified as T, while so-called T-cell CLL remains quite exceptional since we found only two such cases out of 45 typical CLL investigated for membrane markers.

Table 5. Four different membrane phenotypes in human neoplastic hematological disorders

| I | mIg (-), Fc ag Ig (-)[x], C$_3$ (-), E (+), Em (-) | T |
|---|---|---|
| II | mIg (+), Fc ag Ig (+), C$_3$ (+), E (-), Em (+) | B |
| III | mIg (-), Fc ag Ig (-), C$_3$ (-), E (-), Em (-) | NDMM |
| IV | mIg (-), Fc ag Ig (+), C$_3$ (+), E (-), Em (-) | ? |

(x) may be (+) on certain T neoplastic cells.

For abbreviations, see Table 2.

Table 6. T-cell neoplastic disorders

Observed membrane phenotype: mIg (-), Fc ag Ig (-), Fc (-), C$_3$ (-), E (+)

| 1. Primary immunoblastic ALL | 25% | 1/4[a] |
|---|---|---|
| 2. Typical primary ALL | 23% | 7/30 |
| 3. Non leukemic and leukemic LS | 16% | 5/31 |
| 4. BLastic crisis of CML | 16% | 1/6 |
| 5. CLL | 4% | 2/45 |
| Total | 10.6% | 16/150 |

[a] Fc ag Ig (+)

## 2.2. B-cell Neoplasia (Group II)

Table 7 summarizes our data. In addition to myeloma and primary macroglobulinemia, which we confirmed in all cases studied to be, as expected, B-cell diseases, we showed that most cases of other B-cell proliferations concern CLL and leukemic and nonleukemic LS.

All these disorders have been shown to be monoclonal, most often of the IgM type, since the same immunoglobulin has been detected on the majority of neoplastic cells. In CLL (Table 8) the membrane IgM was often found to be associated with an IgD of the same light chains, while this association was less frequent in the case of leukemic and nonleukemic LS (7, 8).

Table 7. B-cell neoplastic disorders

| Observed membrane phenotype: mIg (+), Fc (+), $C_3'$ (+), E (−) | | |
|---|---|---|
| 1. Myeloma (Kahler) | 100% | 3/3[a] |
| 2. Primary macroglobulinemia (Waldenström) | 100% | 2/2 |
| 3. CPL (with macroglobulinemia) | | 1/1 |
| 4. CLL | 88% | 40/45 |
| 5. Non leukemic and leukemic LS | 58% | 18/31 |
| 6. Hairy cell leukemia | 50% | 2/4 |
| 7. Primary immunoblastic ALL | 25% | 1/4 |
| Total | 44% | 67/150 |

[a] Positive intracytoplasmic immunofluorescence.

2.3. Neoplastic Disorders with no Detectable Membrane Markers (Group III) are presented in Table 9. This category of disease includes all cases of AML (19/19) and all cases of RS (2/2) which were studied, as well as a majority of cases of primary typical ALL (23/30) and of blastic crisis of CML (5/6). Note that in 26% of cases of nonleukemic LS (8/31) there were no detectable T and B membrane markers. A similar result was found in one case of CLL.

Table 8. Immunological heterogeneity in chronic lymphoid leukemia (CLL) according to membrane markers

I  -  40/45 cases: B CLL because of prevalence of mIg (+) cells

II  -  36/40 cases monoclonal:
    IgM: 29,  IgG: 6,  IgA: 1,  Mixed pattern: 4

III  -  ALL mIg (+) cells do not possess other receptors
    mIg (+),   Fc ag Ig (+),   $C_3$ (+),   Em (+)
    85%        30%            40%          51&

IV  -  Monoclonal Ig D with the same light chain are detected on 15 to 80% of IgM (+) cells

V  -  5/45 cases: CLL without B membrane markers
        2 cases: T  CLL because of prevalence of E-rosette-forming cells
        3 cases: unclassififed CLL because of absence of detectable T and B cell membrane markers

Table 9. Neoplastic disorders with no detectable membrane markers

Observed membrane phenotype: mIg (-), Fc ag Ig (-), $C_3$ (-), E (-)

| | | |
|---|---|---|
| 1. AML | 100% | 19/19[a] |
| 2. RS | 100% | 2/2 |
| 3. Blastic crisis of CML | 83% | 5/6 |
| 4. Primary ALL | 76% | 23/30 |
| 5. Primary IALL | 50% | 2/4 |
| 6. AML | 50% | 1/2 |
| 7. Leukemic and non leukemic LS | 26% | 8/31 |
| 8. CLL | 2% | 1/45[b] |
| Total | 40% | 61/150 |

[a] Including AMML

[b] RFC with murine RBC

2.4. Neoplastic Disorders with Complement and/or Fc Receptors (Group IV)
Results dealing with this group are presented in Table 10. There are
two cases of HCL, two cases of CLL, one case of AMoL, and one case of
CMoL.

Table 10. Neoplastic disorders with activated complement and/or Fc
receptors

| | | |
|---|---|---|
| I. Observed membrane phenotype: mIg (-), Fc ag Ig (+), $C_3$ (+), E (-) | | |
| Hairy cell leukemia | 50% | 2/4 |
| Chronic lymphoid leukemia | 4% | 2/45 |
| II. Observed membrane phenotype: mIg (-), Fc ag Ig (-), $C_3$ (+), E (-) | | |
| Acute monocytoid leukemia | 50% | 1/2 |
| Chronic monocytoid leukemia | | 1/1 |
| Total | 4% | 6/150 |

DISCUSSION

From the data reported here, hematological neoplastic disorders have
been classified into three main groups, the T- and B-cell neoplasia,

and a third group of null cell disorders characterized by the proliferation of neoplastic cells having no detectable T- or B-membrane markers.

This immunological classification led us to several conclusions.

1. B-cell neoplasias are the most frequent diseases in our series, since they represent about 50% of the cases studied.

All the B-cell proliferations have been found to be monoclonal, confirming other reports (1, 38).

In our series, the monoclonal Ig was most often of the IgM type, and this monoclonal IgM was found to be associated in several cases studied with an IgD having the same light chain, also confirming other reports (17, 30, 36).

Except for some cases including IALL (23) and lymphosarcomas (8), all the disorders of this group have been found to possess various common characteristics. They occur in adults, they have a chronic and subacute evolution, and the neoplastic cells have a relatively well-differentiated feature. These disorders, however, may be related to different neoplastic processes. There is a temptation to assume, like SALMON and SELIGMANN (37), that these various proliferations may be due to the blocking of the B-cell maturation, at different levels, but this concept needs further investigation.

2. In contrast, T-cell neoplasias are less frequent since this group represents only about 10% of our series. Except for two cases of CLL, this group is composed of acute diseases including leukemias and non-Hodgkin's hematosarcomas. It is worth mentioning that most of the patients in this group are children or young adults (8, 23).

These observations suggest that T-cell diseases may be related to thymic anomalies since they affect young patients whose thymus should normally be functional and since experimental data exist demonstrating the role of the thymus in animal leukemogenesis (3, 21). This hypothesis needs, however, further experimental confirmation.

3. In our series, 40% of the cases have not been classified as T- or B-cell diseases, and thus have been called "null" cell disorders. Except for one case of CLL, this group was found to be composed of cases of acute leukemias and of 26% of non-Hodgkin's hematosarcomas studied. This data led us to hypothesize that this group of null cell disorders may, in fact, cover two types of diseases.

The first type includes nonlymphoid neoplastic proliferation, i.e., diseases of myeloid and monocytoid origin, since all the AML cases investigated for T and B membrane markers were included in this group. In contrast, the second type may be composed of true lymphoid disorders in which neoplastic cells are characterized by a lack (or a loss) of T or B membrane markers, probably due to modifications induced through the neoplastic process: this hypothesis could explain the presence of several cases of undifferentiated leukemias and non-Hodgkin's hematosarcomas in this group.

The individualization of null diseases, however, raises the question of the existence of undifferentiated diseases not related either to the lymphoid or to the myelomonocytoid series. These may be disorders of the stem cells (14).

It is evident that more sophisticated investigations including the use of cytochemistry (8, 12) and of specific hetero-antisera (20, 27) will be helpful in elucidating this problem.

4. We described a fourth group of neoplasias which includes a limited number of cases (4% of our series). In this group, the neoplastic cells possess activated receptors for complement and/or Fc receptors and thus could not be definitely typed as B-lymphocytes or monocytes in nature. It is believed that these disorders may, in fact, have a B-lymphoid or monocytoid origin and that the lack (or the loss) of the other markers of the B or monocytoid series may be due to the occurence of a time-related functional variation of the synthesis of these receptors.

From this data it is obvious that it is through an extended use of such immunological investigations that progress will be made in the improvement of classification and physiopathological understanding of lympho-monocytoid proliferative disorders. However, definite progress cannot be achieved if immunological data are not correlated with other parameters such as the clinical picture, the prognostic factors, as well as the results of cytology, histology, and other methods. The search for such a correlation between clinical and morphological data are the subject of the following papers (7, 8, 25).

REFERENCES

1. Aisenberg, A.C., Long, J.C.: Lymphocyte surface characteristics in malignant lymphoma. Amer. J. Med. 58, 300 (1975)
2. Belpomme, D., Dantchev, D., Du Rusquec, E., Grandjon, D., Huchet, R., Pouillart, P., Schwarzenberg, L., Amiel, J.L., Mathé, G.: T and B lymphocyte markers on the neoplastic cell of 20 patients with acute and 10 patients with chronic lymphoid leukemia. Biomed. 20, 109 (1974)
3. Belpomme, D., Dantchev, D., Du Rusquec, E., Grandjon, D., Huchet, R., Pinon, F., Pouillart, P., Schwarzenberg, L., Amiel, J.L., Mathé, G.: La nature T ou B des cellules néoplastiques des leucémies lymphoides. Bull. Cancer 61, 387 (1974)
4. Belpomme, D., Dantchev, D., Joseph, R., Huchet, R., Santoro, A., Grandjon, D., Mathé, G.: Further studies of acute and chronic leukemias: T and B cell membrane markers and scanning electron microscopy. In: Current studies in standardization. Problems in clinical pathology, haematology and radiotherapy in Hodgkin's disease. Astaldi, G., Biagini, C., Cammisa, M., Tentori, L., Torlontano, G., (eds.). Amsterdam: Excerpta Medica, 1975, Vol. I, p. 143
5. Belpomme, D., Dantchev, D., Joseph, R., Lelarge, N., Feuilhade De Chauvin, F., Grandjon, D., Mathé, G.: Cell membrane markers of T and B lymphocytes and monocytes in leukemias and hematosarcomas. Amsterdam: Excerpta Medica, 1975, Vol. I
6. Belpomme, D., Dantchev, D., Joseph, R., Santoro, A., Feuilhade De Chauvin, F., Lelarge, N., Grandjon, D., Pontvert, D., Mathé, G.: Classification of leukemias and hematosarcomas based on membrane markers and scanning electron microscopy. In: Clinical tumor immunology. Oxford: Pergamon press, 1976, Vol. I, p. 131
7. Belpomme, D., Dantchev, D., Karima, A.M., Lelarge, N., Joseph, R., Caillou, B., Lafleur, N., and Mathé, G.: Search for Correlations Between Immunological and Morphological Criteria Used to Classify Lymphoid Leukemias and Non-Hodgkin's Hematosarcomas, With Special Reference to Scanning Electron Microscopy and T and B Membrane Markers, 1976 in preparation.

8. Belpomme et al.: T Cell Marker, a prognostic factor complementary to morphologic differentiation in non-mediastinal acute lymphoid leukaemia (ALL). Is T-ALL a clinical entity? 1976. In preparation

9. Bianco, C., Patrick, R., Nussenzweig, V.: A population of lymphocytes bearing a membrane receptor for antigen-antibody complement complexes. I. Separation and characterization. J. Exp. Med. 132, 702 (1970)

10. Brain, P., Gordon, J., Willetts, W.A.: Rosette formation by peripheral lymphocytes. Clin. Exp. Immunol. 6, 681 (1970)

11. Brown, G., Greaves, M.F., Lister, T.A., Rapson, N., Papamichael, M.: Expression of human T and B lymphocyte cell surface markers on leukemic cells. Lancet 2, 753 (1974)

12. Catovsky, D.: T cell origin of acid phosphate positive lymphoblasts. Lancet 2, 929 (1975)

13. Dantchev, D.: Revised semiology of the different mononuclear cells under scanning electron microscopy. Europ. J. Cancer, in press, 1976

14. Davis, D.: Hypothesis: Differentiation of the human lymphoid system based on cell surface markers. Blood 45, 871 (1975)

15. Dickler, H.B., Siegal, F.P., Bentwich, Z.H., Kunkel, H.G.: Lymphocyte binding of aggregated IgG and surface Ig staining in chronic lymphocytic leukemia. Clin. Exp. Immunol. 14, 97 (1973)

16. Froland, S., Natvig, J.B.: Surface-bound immunoglobulin as a marker of B lymphocytes in man. Nature (New Biol.) 234, 251 (1971)

17. Fu, S.M., Winchester, R.J., Kunkel, H.G.: Occurrence of surface IgM, IgD and free light chains on human lymphocytes. J. Exp. Med. 139, 451 (1974)

18. Hainz, H.: Human monocytes: distinct receptor sites for the third component of complement and for immunoglobulin G. Science 162, 1281 (1968)

19. Jondal, M., Holm, G., Wigzell, H.: A large population of lymphocytes forming non-immune rosettes with sheep red blood cells. J. Exp. Med. 136, 207 (1972)

20. Kersey, J.H., Coccia, P.F., Gajl-Peczalska, K.J., Hallgreen, H., Krivit, W., Yunis, E., Nesbit, M.E.: Childhood lymphoproliferative malignancies: the definition of three distinct groups by cell surface markers. In: Fourth Annual Conference of International Society for Experimental Hematology, Yugoslavia, Sept. 1975 (abstract 105) p. 46

21. Mathé, G., Belpomme, D.: T and B lymphocytic nature of leukemias and lymphosarcomas: a new but still uncertain parameter for their classification. Biomed. 20, 81 (1974)

22. Mathé, G., Belpomme, D., Dantchev, D., Pouillart, P., Jasmin, C., Misset, J.L., Musset, M., Amiel, J.L., Schlumberger, J.R., Schwarzenberg, L., Hayat, M., De Vassal, F., Lafleur, M.: Immunoblastic acute lymphoid leukemia. Biomed. 20, 333 (1974)

23. Mathé, G., Belpomme, D., Dantchev, D., Pouillart, P.: Progress in the classification of lymphoid and/or monocytoid leukemias and of lympho- and reticulosarcomas (non-Hodgkin's lymphomas). Biomed. 22, 177 (1975)

24. Mathé, G., Belpomme, D., Dantchev, D., Pouillart, P., Schlumberger, J.R., Lafleur, M.: Leukemic lymphosarcomas: respective prognosis of the three types: prolymphocytic, lymphoblastic (or lymphoblastoid) and immunoblastic. Blood Cells 1, 25 (1975)

25. Mathé, G., Dantchev, D.: Non-Hodgkin's haematosarcoma. Classification of the W.H.O. reference center for neoplastic diseases of hemopoietic and lymphoid tissues. This volume, 1976

26. Mathé, G., Rappaport, H.: Histological and cytological typing of the neoplastic diseases of the hematopoietic and lymphoid tissues. Geneva: W.H.O., 1976, Vol. I

27. Metzgar, R.S., Mohanakumar, T., Miller, D.S.: Antigens specific for human lymphocytic and myeloid leukemia cells: detection by non human primate antiserums. Sciences 178, 986 (1972)

28. Perlman, P., Biberfeld, P., Larsson, A., Perlman, H., Wahlin, B.: Surface markers of antibody dependent lymphocytic effectors cells (K cells) in human blood. In: Membrane receptors of lymphocytes. Seligmann, M., Preud'homme, J.L., Kourilsky, F.M., (eds.). Inserm Symp. Amsterdam: North-Holland and New York: Elsevier, 1975, Vol. I, p. 161

29. Peter, C.R., Mac Kenzie, M.R.: T or B cell origin of some non-Hodgkin's lymphomas. Lancet 2, 686 (1974)

30. Preud'homme, J.L., Brouet, J.C., Clauvel, J.P., Šeligmann, M.: Surface IgD in immunoproliferative disorders. Scand J. Immunol. 3, 853 (1874)

31. Preud'homme, J.L., Seligmann, M.: Surface bound immunoglobulin as a cell marker in human proliferative diseases. Blood 40, 777 (1972)

32. Raff, M.C.: Two distinct populations of peripheral lymphocytes in mice distinguishable by immunofluorescence. Immunol. 19, 637 (1970)

33. Report of a WHO/IARC sponsored Workshop on human B and T cells, London 1974. Identification, enumeration and isolation of B and T lymphocytes from human peripheral blood. Scand J. Immunol. 3, 521 (1974)

34. Revillard, J.P., Samarut, C., Cordier, G., Brochier, J.: Characterization of human bearing Fc receptors with special reference to cytotoxic (K) cells. In: Membrane receptors of lymphocytes. Seligmann, M., Preud'homme, J.L., Kourilsky, F.M., (eds.). Inserm Symp. Amsterdam: North-Holland and New York: Elsevier, 1975, Vol. I, p. 171

35. Ross, G.D., Rabellino, E.M., Polley, M.J., Grey, H.M.: Combined studies of complement receptor and surface immunoglobulin bearing cells and sheep erythrocyte rosette forming cells in normal and leukemic human lymphocytes. J. Clin. Invest. 52, 377 (1973)

36. Rowe, D.S., Hug, K., Forni, L., Pernis, B.: Immunoglobulin D as a lymphocyte receptor. J. Exp. Med. 138, 965 (1973)

37. Salmon, S.E., Seligmann, M.: B-cell neoplasia in man. Lancet 2, 1230 (1974)

38. Seligmann, M., Preud'homme, J.L., Brouet, J.C.: B and T cell markers in human proliferative blood diseases and primary immunodeficiencies, with special reference to membrane bound immunoglobulins. Transplant Rev. 16, 85 (1973)

39. Wilson, J.D., Nossal, G.J.V.: Identification of human T and B lymphocytes in normal peripheral blood and in chronic lymphocytic leukemia. Lancet 2, 788 (1971)

40. Wybran, J., Can, M.C., Fudenberg, H.H.: The human rosette forming cells as a marker of a population of thymus derived cells. J. Clin. Invest. 51, 2537 (1972)

# Chapter 15

# Hodgkin's Disease: A War Between T-Lymphocytes and Transformed Macrophages?

M. M. B. KAY

ABSTRACT

The interaction between Reed-Sternberg (RS) cells and autogeneic T
T cells was investigated. It was found that T cells cytolyse RS cells
in the following sequential manner: Stage 1, T cells affix the tips
of their microvilli onto target cells; Stage 2, T cells subject cell
membranes to tearing and shearing forces which produce gaps and holes;
Stage 3, target cells lyse and T cells "crawl" away. The relationship
between the events occurring at the cellular level and those observed
clinically are discussed.

Hodgkin's disease holds a fascination for clinicians and "bench" scien-
tists alike, perhaps because of the enigma and challenge it represents.
It is not surprising, therefore, that many questions go unanswered.
For example, we are still addressing ourselves to the following questions: What is the origin of the Reed-Sternberg (RS) cell? If a macrophage, then why do T cells attach to it and what is the nature of the
T cell-RS interaction? Why is cellular immunity so often impaired
even in patients in the early stages of the disease? Why do patients
with Hodgkin's disease sometimes develop autoimmune hemolytic anemia
when they are, in fact, immunologically hyporesponsive? In this paper,
I shall present evidence which answers a few of these questions and
provides hypothetical answers to the others.

## MATERIALS AND METHODS

Cells were dissociated from involved lymph nodes of individuals with
untreated Hodgkin's disease, washed 3 times with RPMI-1640 without
serum, resuspended in the same media, pipetted onto round glass coverslips inside petri dishes, and incubated at 37°C in 5% $CO_2$. Samples
were processed at 5, 10, 20, and 30 min. as described previously (11,
13, 14). Each coverslip was then viewed with a Zeiss photomicroscope
operated in the phase mode. The location of RS cells was noted for
viewing with scanning electron microscopy (SEM). Cells having all of
the following features were considered to be RS cells: (a) two or more
nuclei, (b) thick nuclear membranes, (c) abundant cytoplasm, and (d)
large, round or oval nucleoli surrounded by a perinuclear halo in each
nucleus (Fig. 1 and inset). Such cells were generally significantly
larger than the surrounding cells, and were, therefore, easily localed
with SEM (13).

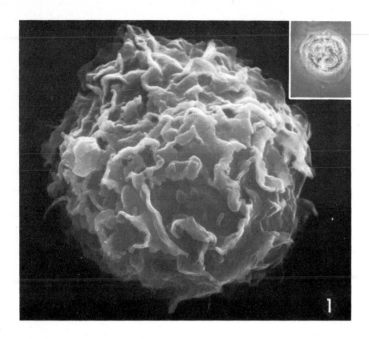

*Fig. 1. RS cell with lamellae (x 5,440). Phase microscopy (inset) de-
monstrates the identifying features of RS cells in SEM preparations:
(a) two nuclei, (b) thick nuclear membranes, (c) abundant, "foamy"
cytoplasm, and (d) large, oval nucleoli (x 896)*

Approximately 200 RS cells were viewed at each time interval. No attempt was made to assess the specificity of killer T cells against
target RS cells because of technical limitations, e.g., sparsity of
non-RS histiocytes. Specimens were viewed with an Hitachi HFS SEM operated at 20 KV.

Lymphocytes attacking target cells were defined as T cells because:
(a) they fluoresced when treated with fluorescent labeled anti-T cell
sera, (b) they did not fluoresce when treated with fluorescent labeled
anti-B cell reagent prepared against chronic lymphocytic leukemia
cells, (c) they formed nonimmune sheep erythrocyte (E) rosettes, and
(d) they met the SEM criteria set forth previously (10, 13, 18). The
RS cells, which are 3-4 times larger than lymphocytes, were defined as
histiocytic cells because they did not fluoresce with fluorescent anti-
T cell reagent, did not form nonimmune E rosettes, did fluoresce with
fluorescent anti-B cell reagent, met the SEM criteria for macrophages
(10, 13, 18), and phagocytized lymphocytes (13).

RESULTS

After 5 min. of culture, the tips of microvilli of T cells were in
contact with the lamellae (ruffles) and filopodia of RS cells (Fig. 2A
and B) and an average of about 6 T cells were in contact with each
RS cell. The membranes of RS cells appeared intact as no holes or gaps
were visible.

112

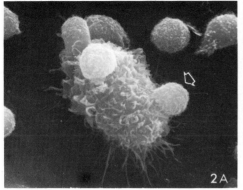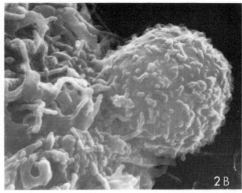

*Fig. 2. Cells were cultured and samples were fixed as described in the text. Samples were postfixed with 1% ruthenium red-3% GA, dehydrated with ethanol, critical-point dried and coated with 5 nm of gold-palladium in an Edward's evaporator with planetary stage. Specimens were viewed with an Hitachi Hi Scan operated at 15-20 KV. Micrographs were recorded on Polaroid 55P/N film; (A) RS cell with lamellae and filopodia after 5 min. of culture (x 4,000); (B) Higher magnification of lymphocyte indicated arrow in Fig. 2A shows lymphocyte attached by microvilli to RS cell membrane (x 15,000)*

After 10 min. of culture, it was evident that the cells had firmly attached their microvilli to RS cells. It appeared as if the membranes of RS cells were being "pulled apart", creating gaps (Fig. 3A, B, and C). As a consequence of the formation of gaps, the width of which ranged from 2-4 nm, globular membrane subunits became visible at high magnification (Fig. 2B).

On occasions globular subunits were separated by 18 nm-wide gaps, giving the appearance of a "hole" in the membrane. After 15 min. of culture, RS cells lost all their lamellae and assumed a spherical shape (Fig. 3D). The proportion of T cells decreased to about 1.5 for every one RS cell, and the interglobular gaps increased in width to about 15 nm (range, 13-18 nm) and the holes to 50-100 nm.

By 20 min. of culture, the minimum interglobular gaps were 40-60 nm in width and aggregates of globular units became separated from the matrix, leaving gaping holes as wide as 900 nm (Fig. 4A and inset). It was apparent by this time that the membranes of RS cells were disintegrating. At 30 min. all that remained of the membranes of RS cells were disorganized, loosely associated globular subunits around nuclei and scattered cytoplasmic organelles (Fig. 4B).

Measurements of cell size showed that RS cells increased from an average of 9 μm in diameter (range, 8-10 μm) after 5 min. of culture to an average of 15 μm in diameter after 20 min. of culture, just before the cells began to disintegrate. With regard to cell size, it should be noted that cells prepared for SEM are not "stretched" as are cells prepared by smears and, therefore, generally appear smaller.

These results indicate that killer T cells cytolyse autologous neoplastic RS target cells in the following sequential manner ultrastructurally: Stage 1, T cells affix the tips of their microvilli onto target cells; Stage 2, cells subject target cell membranes to tearing

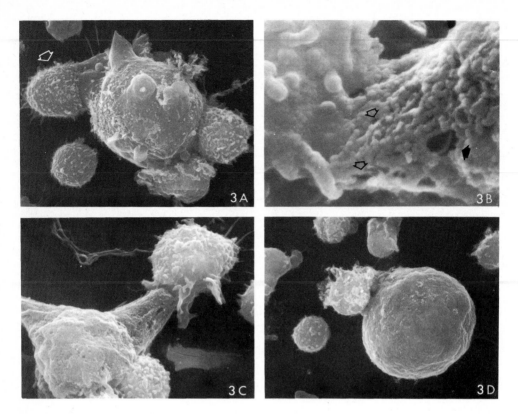

*Fig. 3(A). RS cell at 10 min. with lymphocytes attached by microvilli.*
*Lymphocyte at upper left is firmly attached both to the substate and*
*RS cell by microvilli, and has pulled away a large area of the RS*
*membrane. Most of the RS cell's lamellae have collapsed (x 3,700);*
*3(B) Higher magnification of junction between T cell and RS cell indi-*
*cated arrow in Fig. 3A shows (1) intact lymphocyte membrane which ap-*
*pears homogeneous without visible subunit architecture, (2) microvilli*
*of lymphocyte pulling RS cell membrane on which (3) subunit architecture*
*is visible because of gaps between subunits, and (4) holes in membrane*
*(arrows) (x 50,000); 3(C) RS cell devoid of lamellae and filopodia at*
*15 min.. It is spherical except for membrane which is being torn by*
*T cells. Gaping holes have appeared on areas adjacent to killer cells*
*(x 5,000); 3(D) Spherical RS cell devoid of lamellae at 15 min.*
*(x 3,300). One lymphocyte with subunits from RS membrane remains on*
*RS cell*

and shearing forces which produce gaps progressing to holes between
the membrane subunits. An interpretation of the formation of gaps and
holes is that they allow leakage of ions, resulting in an increase
in intracellular osmotic pressure which can lead to an influx of the
extracellular fluid. This, in turn, can cause osmotic swelling of the
cells forcing them to take on a spherical shape (27); Stage 3, target
cells lyse as a result of further stretching of the membrane caused by
increasing internal osmotic pressure, and T cells "crawl" away.

However, in this battle for the lymph node, the T cells do not always
win and crawl away. RS cells have been observed to phagocytize lymphocytes. Moreover, the incidence of phagocytosis was high when the

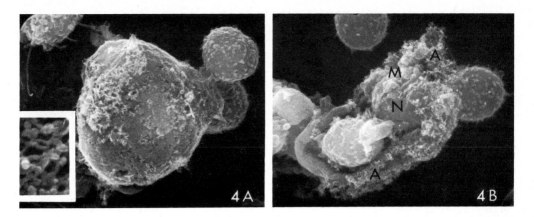

Fig. 4(A) At 20 min. RS cell membranes are visibly disintegrating even at low magnification (x 5,000) and gaping holes are visible; 4(B) RS cell at 30 min.: nucleus (N), mitochodria (M), surrounded by a "fuzz" of membrane aggregates (A), all that remains of membrane (x 5,000)

relative RS cell surface area occupied by lymphocytes was low. Thus, it was noted that lymphocytes were generally phagocytized where only one was attached to an RS cell, but none was phagocytized when 6 or more lymphocytes were attached. In the latter situation, lymphocytes literally seemed to "grasp" the RS cell's membrane and pull on it (Fig. 3A and 3C). This appears to "frustate" RS cells in their attempt to phagocytize the lymphocytes.

Occasionally, "normal" macrophages and/or monocytes (i.e., those that do not meet the criteria of RS cells) were attacked by lymphocytes (Fig. 5 and inset). This is unusual as I have observed with SEM over

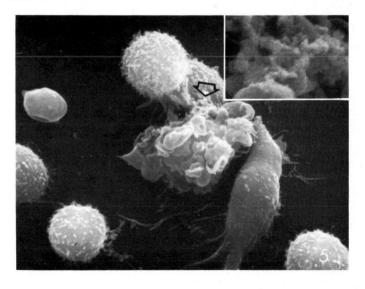

Fig. 5. Monocyte with lymphocytes attached (x 3,770). Inset shows membrane particles (x 20,000)

3,000 macrophages from normal individuals, and have not observed lymphocytes "pulling" on their membranes. Further, these "normal" macrophages and monocytes possess membrane particles (inset Fig. 5) often observed on RS cells, which I have not observed on macrophages of normal individuals when prepared by the same techniques. This suggests the possibility that "normal" macrophages and monocytes in Hodgkin's disease may be expressing altered surface antigens. If so, the possibility exists that macrophages of patient's with Hodgkin's disease may have been infected with a virus which they were unable to digest after engulfment. This possibility is not unreasonable for it is known that certain viruses can proliferate preferentially inside macrophages (5, 7).

DISCUSSION

The evidence presented here indicates that "killer" T cells cytolyse RS target cells in the following sequential manner: Stage 1, T cells affix the tips of their microvilli onto target cells; Stage 2, T cells subject target cell membranes to tearing and shearing forces which produce gaps and holes; Stage 3, target cells lyse and T cells "crawl" away.

Four comments are in order regarding the ultrastructural sequence of events reported here. (i) Lymphocytes have been reported in close contact with RS cells in surgical biopsy specimens fixed immediately upon removal (1). This would suggest that the information obtained in this study could be describing the in situ events rather accurately. (ii) That the cytolytic reaction is mediated by lymphocyte microvilli is consistent with the previous observation that receptors for cellular interaction of T cells reside on the proximal portion of their microvilli (11). (iii) The events observed here agree remarkably well with the biochemical data reported previously by FERLUGA and ALLISON (6). They showed that leakage of ions occurs early and peaks between 10-15 min. and this is followed by leakage of macromolecules at about 10 min. which increases in a linear fashion. (iv) The findings that cytolysis of target cells is mediated by T-cell microvilli is consistent with a previous report (8) that cytocholasin B, a drug that inhibits microfilament function (30) and causes partial or complete collapse of T-cell microvilli (17), inhibits T cell-target cell interaction (i.e., Stage 1). Colchicine, which binds to microtubules (3) and inhibits membrane lamellae while sparing microvilli (17) does not inhibit T-cell attachment to target cells but inhibits target-cell killing (8), presumably by inhibiting Stage 2 as described above.

In a previous communication based on light and transmission electron microscopy study of cytolysis of neoplastic mastocytoma cells by allogeneic spleen cells (19), it was reported that close contact between lymphocytes and target cells occurred after 1 h of culture and that target cells manifested damage after 2-4 h of culture. Clearly, the cytolytic events reported here occurred more rapidly. The difference in kinetics of cytolysis of target cells may be due to a variety of causes including differences in: (a) culture conditions, (b) preparation of cell suspensions, (c) sensitivity of detection methods, (d) type of target cells (allogeneic versus autogeneic), and (e) presence of B cells in the reaction culture. In regard to the latter, B cells could have participated in the cytolysis of allogeneic target cells but not in the killing of autogeneic target cells as described here. In the former, spleen cells were employed and it is known that there are more B than T cells in the spleen of mice (25). Moreover, it was observed that vesicles containing cytoplasmic droplets were being released with increasing frequency during cytolysis of the allogeneic target cells. In this study, only T cells were detected attacking the target cells, as judged by four different criteria, and no release of cytoplasmic droplets was observed during cytolysis of autologous target cells. However, even though B cells were not observed in contact with RS cells during Stages 1 and 2 and although antibody and complement were not present in the culture medium, the participation of B cells cannot be entirely excluded.

The results presented here suggest that cytolysis of autogeneic target tumor cells is mediated by T-cell microvilli through which tearing and shearing forces are transmitted. The gaps and holes produced by these forces between the membrane subunits allow leakage of ions and influx of fluid resulting in target-cell lysis by osmotic swelling.

In order to successfully cytolyse RS cells, it appears that the T cell to target cell ratio must be greater than 3; otherwise, the T cells themselves can be attacked and destroyed. Thus, it takes many T cells to kill one RS cell, but one RS cell can kill many lymphocytes. The phagocytosis of lymphocytes by RS cells could account for the impaired cellular immunity and lymphocyte depletion seen in advanced disease. Further, it would explain the poor prognosis of the "mixed type" of Hodgkin's disease, i.e., shift in the ratio favoring the RS cell can lead to lymphocyte depletion.

Based on the findings, it is my suspicion that the histologic classification in Hodgkin's disease is time-dependent. In other words, I think that, initially, lymphocytes predominate. If they fail to destroy the malignant cells, the latter cells would proliferate and, consequently, biopsy would reveal "mixed cellularity." "Lymphocyte depletion," resulting from the phagocytosis of lymphocytes by RS cells, would logically follow since the RS cells would win on sheer size and number. Nodular sclerosis may present a "burned out," quiescent Hodgkin's disease (i.e., the lymphocytes had won the battle and the "battleground," and the remaining RS cells are enclosed in a granuloma by the fibroblasts and normal macrophages). This hypothesis is consistent with the survival statistics available on the various histologic classifications (i.e., lymphocyte predominant and nodular sclerosis have the best prognosis, while mixed type and lymphocyte depletion have the worst). In this regard, it is interesting to note that in the series of 25 patients studied by ZIEGLER et al. (31), only 2 out of 12 (17%) of the patients with lymphocyte predominant Hodgkin's disease were anergic, and these were in Stage 3B and 4B. The average number of positive responses to 4 skin-test antigens in this series was 2.48, ± 0.17 (standard error of the mean) for 25 normal controls; 2.17, ± 0.37 for lymphocyte predominant; 0.25, ± 0.16 for mixed cellularity; and 0.0 for lymphocyte depleted. The destruction of RS cells by "killer" T cells might, in part, account for the success of radiotherapy - radiotherapy probably reduces the load of malignant cells to the point where the T cells can handle the rest. This could also explain the limited success in patients with advanced disease whose cytotoxic T cells may have been destroyed by the RS cells. The fact that older patients often have disease which is in unfavorable histologic or staging categories is consistent with the data demonstrating decreased T-cell function in older individuals (21, 26).

The autoimmune hemolytic anemia that is sometimes seen in patients with Hodgkin's disease and in patients with lymphocytic lymphoma or chronic lymphocytic leukemia may be a direct result of a deficiency in cellular immunity. I have hypothesized previously (16) that decreased T-cell responsiveness permits the ingress of viruses, for T cells are, in part, responsible for host immunity to such microbes as, for example, viruses. Because these invasive viruses are not destroyed rapidly, they have access to the blood and tissues. I believe that viral enzymes, such as the neuraminidase of influenza virus, can cleave molecules, such as sialic acid, off cell surfaces thus exposing carbohydrates to which B cells can produce antibody without T-cell assistance (B cells can produce antibody without T-cell collaboration when the antigen consists of repetitive, monotonous subunits, as is the case with carbohydrates and polysaccharides). Experiments performed in my laboratory have shown that circulating old RBC have autogeneic immunoglobulin (IgG) (presumably autoantibody) attached to their surface (12, 15). When young RBC are treated with neuraminidase, IgG attaches to them, initiating their removal by macrophages (Fig. 6) just as though they were old RBC (Table 1). This could be the mechanism by which immunologically hyporesponsive patients with lymphoproliferative disorders develop autoimmune hemolytic anemia or thrombocytopenia, which, when viewed superficially, appears paradoxical.

Table 1

| RBC | Culture medium | % Phagocytosis |
|-----|----------------|----------------|
| YRBC | 199 | 5 ± 2 |
| ORBC | 199 | 33 ± 1.5 |
| YRBC + VCN | 199 | 0 |
| YRBC + VCN | 199 + IgG | 87.33 ± 8.97 |

Relative susceptibility to phagocytosis of old red blood cells (ORBC) aged in situ, young RBC (YRBC), and YRBC pretreated with Vibrio cholerae neuraminidase (YRBC + VCN). For details, see ref. 26.

Phagocytosis of lymphocytes by RS cells raises yet another question; i.e., what is the mechanism by which RS cells bind lymphocytes? It is known that macrophages phagocytize autogeneic RBC only when IgG is attached to the RBC surface (15). It appears that this is the general physiological mechanism by which macrophages recognize altered, damaged, or senescent cells. IgG autoantibody to T cells could be produced by the same mechanism previously discussed for effete RBC as T-lymphocyte membranes are similar to RBC membranes in that they contain relatively high proportions of sialic acid that is susceptible to neuraminidase (22). This is consistent with the findings of LONGMIRE et al. (20), who reported an increase in the in vitro splenic IgG synthesis in patients with Hodgkin's disease and found that the IgG bound to homologous lymphocytes. Unfortunately, they did not employ autogeneic lymphocytes so that the possibility of IgG binding to non-histocompatible membrane antigens cannot be excluded. It is possible that patients with Hodgkin's disease and other immunoproliferative disorders can produce autoantibody which goes undetected until late in the course of the disease because it does not produce clinical symptoms. The lack of clinical symptoms could be due to (a) cellular production keeping pace with destruction or (b) relatively low quantities of IgG that binds relatively little complement. Of course, the possibility that the cells are or become altered, thus invoking IgG binding, cannot be excluded.

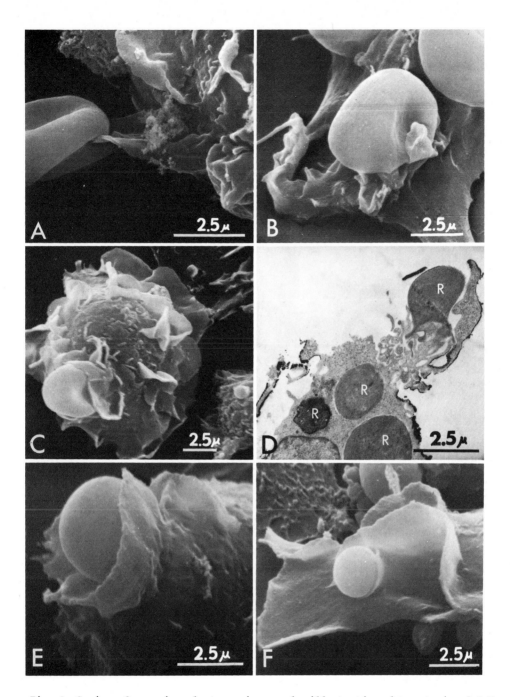

Fig. 6. Series of scanning electron micrographs illustrating phagocytosis of IgG-coated RBC. A lamellipodia from a macrophage contacts an RBC (A) and draws it back toward cell surface where villus processes and filopodia attach to it identing its surface (B). Lamellipodia on macrophage surface flow over and around RBC (C) which is pulled inward by attachments from the initial filopodial and villus processes (D. Tem; R=RBC) and deformed by the lamellipodia flowing over it (E) until only a small (1-2μ), round ball remains of the RBC (F) before another wave of lamellipodia fold over it and engulf it completely

I suggest earlier that RS cells are macrophages that may be infected by a virus. Others have proposed (a) that cells are infected by an oncogenic virus and that these altered T cells are attacked by normal T cells which gives rise to a morphologically distinct malignant histiocytic cell line (23) and (b) that the malignant cell in Hodgkin's disease is itself a T cell (29). It would seem that these hypotheses have to be advocated because they purportedly explain the progressive loss of T-cell responsiveness in Hodgkin's disease. However, the evidence presented here and elsewhere (4, 10, 13, 14, 16) when considered together strongly supports a macrophage origin, and demonstrates that cytotoxic T cells initiate the destruction of RS cells. Progressive loss of T-cell functions is easily explained by T-cell loss through RS cell phagocytosis. The hypothesis presented here, namely, that RS cells are macrophages which ingested a virus that proliferated preferentially in them, is consistent with the facts (5, 7). It could also explain the initiation of the disease in lymph nodes and subsequent dissemination of the disease by direct contiguity to adjacent lymphoid tissue and by lymphatics to distant sites. Further, it explains many of the apparent paradoxes associated with Hodgkin's disease. Finally, it has the advantage of being quite simple.

## REFERENCES

1. Archibald, R.B., Frenster, J.: Qualitative ultrastructural analysis of in vivo lymphocyte-Reed-Sternberg cell interaction in Hodgkin's disease. Natl. Cancer Inst. Monogr. 36, 245 (1973)
2. Bang, F.B., Warwick, A.: Mouse macrophages as host cells for mouse hepatitis virus and the genetic basis of their susceptibility. Proc. nat. Acad. Sci. (Wash.) 46, 1065 (1960)
3. Berlin, R., Ukena, T.: Effect on colchicine and vinblastine on the agglutination of polymorphonuclear leukocytes by concanavalin A. Nature 238, 120 (1972)
4. Dantchev, D., Belpomme, D., Martin, M., Mathé, G.: Immunological studies of Reed-Sternberg cell and lymphocytes in Hodgkin's disease. XV. Congress Int. Soc. Hematol. 427 (1974)
5. De-Thé, G., Notkins, A.L.: Ultrastructure of the lactic dehydrogenase virus (LDV) and cell-virus relationship. Virology 26, 512 (1965)
6. Ferluga, J., Allison, A.C.: Observations on the mechanism by which T-lymphocytes exert cytotoxic effects. Nature 250, 673 (1974)
7. Goodman, G.T., Koprowsky, H.: Macrophages as a cellular expression of inherited natural resistance. Proc. nat. Acad. Sci. (Wash.) 48, 160 (1962)
8. Henny, C., Bubberrs, E.: Antigen-T lymphocyte interaction: Inhibition by cytochalasin B[1,2]. J. Immunol. 111, 85 (1973)
9. Jones, T.C.: Macrophages and intercellular parasitism. J. Reticuloendothel. Soc. 13, 263 (1973)
10. Kadin, M., Newcom, S., Gold, S., Stites, D.: Origin of Hodgkin's cell. Lancet i, 167 (1974)
11. Kay, M.M., Belohradsky, B., Yee, K., Vogel, J., Butcher, D., Wybran, J., Fudenberg, H.: Cellular Interactions: Scanning electron microscopy of human thymus-derived rosette-forming lymphocytes. Clin. Immunol. Immunopathol. 2, 301 (1974)
12. Kay, M.M.B.: Mechanism of macrophage recognition of senescent red cells. Gerontologist 14, 33 (1974)
13. Kay, M.M.B.: Surface characteristics of Hodgkin's cells. Lancet ii, 459 (1975)
14. Kay, M.M.B.: Multiple labeling technique used for kinetic studies of activated human B lymphocytes. Nature 254, 424 (1975)

15. Kay, M.M.B.: Mechanism of removal of senescent cells by human macrophages in situ. Proc. nat. Acad. Sci. (Wash.) 72, 3521-3525 (1975)
16. Kay, M.M.B.: Autoimmune disease: The consequence of deficient T cell function? J. Amer. Geriat. Soc. In press
17. Kay, M.M.B.: unpublished
18. Kay, M.M.B., Kadin, M.: Classification of Hodgkin's cells according to surface characteristics. Lancet i, 7909, 748 (1975)
19. Koren, H.S., Ax, W., Freund-Moelbert, E.: Morphological studies on the contact-induced lysis of target cells. Europ. J. Immunol. 3, 32 (1973)
20. Longmire, R.L., McMillan, R., Yelenosky, R., Armstrong, S., Lang, J.E., Craddock, C.G.: In vitro splenic IgG synthesis in Hodgkin's disease. N. Engl. J. Med. 289, 763 (1973)
21. Makinodan, T., Adler, W.: Effects of aging on the differentiation and proliferation potentials of cells of the immune system. Fed. Proc. 34, 153 (1975)
22. Mehrishi, J.N., Zeiller, K.: Surface molecular components of T and B lymphocytes. Europ. J. Immunol. 4, 474 (1974)
23. Order, S.E., Hellman, S.: Pathogenesis of Hodgkin's disease. Lancet i, 571 (1972)
24. Porter, D.D., Porter, H.G., Deehake, B.B.: Immunofluorescence assay for antigen and antibody in lactic dehydrogenase virus infection of mice. J. Immunol. 102, 431 (1969)
25. Raff, M.C.: Two distinct populations of peripheral lymphocytes in mice distinguishable by immunofluorescence. Immunol. 19, 637 (1970)
26. Roberts-Thopson, I.C., Whittingham, S., Young Chaiyuo, U., MacKay, I.R.: Ageing, immune response, and mortality. Lancet ii, 368 (1974)
27. Seeman, P.: Ultrastructure of membrane lesions in immune lysis, osmotic lysis, and drug-induced lysis. Fed. Proc. 33, 2116 (1974)
28. Silverstein, S.C.: Macrophages and viral immunity. Semin. Hematol. 7, 185 (1970)
29. De Vita, Jr., V.T.: Lymphocyte reactivity in Hodgkin's disease: A lymphocyte civil war. N. Engl. J. Med. 289, 801 (1973)
30. Wessells, N.K., Spooner, J., ASh, M., Bradley, O., Luduena, M., Taylor, E., Wrenn, J., Yamade, M.: Microfilaments in cellular and developmental processes. Science 717, 135 (1971)
31. Ziegler, J.B., Hansen, P., Penny, R.: Intrinsic lymphocyte defect in Hodgkin's disease: Analysis of the phytohemagglutinin dose response. Clin. Immunol. Immunopathol. 3, 451 (1975)

# Chapter 16
# The Significance of the Macrophage Content of Human Tumours

C. L. GAUCI

## INTRODUCTION

Tumour-elicited host responses are of interest from at least two points
of view: (i) they indicate an ability of the host to respond to the
tumour, and (ii) they imply that the tumour is able to stimulate the
host response. Both these factors may be part and partial of a specific
or non-specific event. Nevertheless, with regard to the pathogenesis
and therapy of malignant disease they would appear to be of paramount
importance.

The macrophage/monocyte arm of the host response is of particular interest. It has been shown that the macrophage content of experimentally
induced animal tumours varies considerably (3, 7, 8, 9) and that the
degree of infiltration is inversely related to their facility for metas-
tasising (1). The rat sarcomas which induce a high macrophage infiltration would appear to be those which evoke the greatest degree of host
resistance as determined by the number of tumour cells which a suitably
immunized rat can reject, which has been labelled its "immunogenicity".
The macrophage infiltration of these highly immunogenic tumours is considerably diminished by previously depleting the animals of T-cells (2).
A number of reports have indicated that the macrophage content of a
variety of human tumours may also be worthy of note (4, 12). In this
paper evidence will be presented to underline the interplay between
the immunogenicity of a tumour, T-cell function, and macrophage infiltration. The peripheral blood monocytes in a rat myelogenous leukemia
will be shown to be of host origin and the importance of similar cells
in human acute myelogenous leukemia is postulated. Data concerning the
macrophage content of a variety of human tumours will be presented
which so far supports the hypothesis formulated in experimental animal
work.

## MATERIALS AND METHODS

### Animal Tumours

Two transplantable rat sarcomas, passaged 20 times in syngeneic Hooded
rats, were studied. One was the benzpyrene-induced tumour HSBPA, the
other a methylcholanthrene-induced tumour MC3. The former has been shown
to be more highly immunogenic (1). These were grown intramuscularly
in the hind limbs of Hooded rats and carefully needled biopsied throughout their growth.

122

The rat leukemia, SAL which has been characterized as an acute myelogenous leukemia (10, 14), was grown in the syngeneic female August rat.
$2 \times 10^5$ cells were injected into the sublingual vein and the peripheral
blood cells were studied throughout its growth. These animals died
7-8 days later with a peripheral blast count of between $1-3 \times 10^5$ blast
cells/mm$^3$.

T-cell depleted animals were produced by removing the entire thymus
in the neonatal period. They were subsequently used at the age of 12-15
weeks.

Hybrid rats were produced by crossing August and Marshall rats and
their offspring, F1, were used.


## Studies on Human Acute Leukemias

Peripheral blood from patients with acute myelogenous leukemias was
collected at presentation, usually during leucophoresis on an IBM
cell separator.

Human solid tumours were obtained directly from theatre and used immediately.


## Macrophage/Monocyte Studies

The technique used was based on that described by EVANS (3). Pieces
of fresh tumour were carefully cleaned by removing all fat, necrotic
and unrelated tissue. The remaining fragment was weighed and then finally minced with scalpels. Animal tumours and human tumours, apart from
breast lesions, were disaggregated by treating with 0.1% trypsin and
0.1% collagenase in TC 199 for 1 h at room temperature whilst being me-
chanically stirred. Hyaluronidase was added to breast tumours which
were treated for at least 2 h. The suspension was passed through sterile
gauze and the total cell number calculated. The cells were then extensively washed in TC 199 and finally reconstitued in 10% heat inactivated foetal calf serum in TC 199 to give a final concentration of
$1 \times 10^6$ cells/ml. The cells were incubated on a glass slide which had
a regular pattern of 8 or 16 mm clear wells formed by a thin Teflon
film. In the former 50 µl (and the latter 200 µl) of the cell suspension were placed into each well with an automatic Oxford micropipette.
A number of slides were put up. These were then incubated at 37°C for
4 h in a CO$_2$ incubator. The proportion of macrophages in the tumour
was calculated by counting the adherent cells per well and measuring
the fraction which bound the specific rabbit anti-macrophage serum
(these were species specific), demonstrated by indirect membrane fluorescence. Opsinised sheep red blood cells were added to the adherent cells
in at least four wells and the slides were re-incubated at 37°C for a
further half hour, prior to washing, fixing and staining. There was a
close concordance between the percentage of adherent cells which were
phagocytic and those which bound the anti-macrophage serum, except,
however, for macrophages derived from heavily pigmented melanomas,
where the amount of melanin present in these cells often obscured the
ingested red cells.

The percentage macrophage content of a tumour =

100 x $\dfrac{\text{total number of adherent cells/well}}{\text{total number of cells added/well}}$ x % cells binding specific anti-macrophage serum

Under these conditions 95% of the macrophages in an enzyme-treated
cell suspension adhere to glass.

When peripheral blood cells were used, these were washed, counted and made up to 1 x 10$^6$/ml in 10% foetal calf serum as above, and the same procedure was adopted.

The criteria used for defining a macrophage/monocyte were:
1. Adherent cell not removed by trypsin
2. Phagocytic
3. Binds species specific anti-macrophage serum
4. Has surface Fc receptors
5. Morphology and histochemical stain

## RESULTS

Relationship between Tumour Immunogenicity, T-Cell Function and Macrophage Infiltration in Rat Sarcomas

When the HSBPA tumour is grown in normal Hooded rats it is clear that the macrophage content remains relatively constant throughout its growth. However, in thymectomised rats the macrophage infiltration is reduced (Fig. 1) and becomes even further diminished as the tumour enlarges. It was also noted that the thymectomised animals developed distant metastases, which is very uncommon with this tumour in T-cell competent animals. The discrepancy between the macrophage and actual malignant cell content in relation to the total cell mass is due to the presence of neutrophils and lymphocytes which decrease in number as the fraction of malignant cells in the tumour increases. Locally recurrent tumours at the site of surgical amputation contain the same degree of macrophage infiltration as the primary tumour from which they arose. The less immunogenic tumour, MC3, has a lower macrophage content, 10% as opposed to 50% in the HSBPA (Fig. 2), and the degree of macrophage infiltration is unaffected by thymectomy. Following surgical amputation, these tumours invariably metastasise. These results

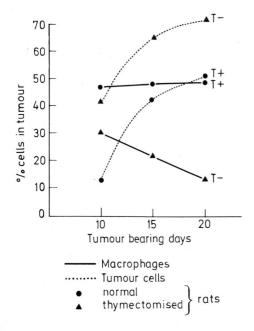

Fig. 1. Macrophage content of immunogenic, benzpyrene-induced rat sarcoma grown in normal and thymectomised syngeneic Hooded rats. Tumours were biopsied throughout growth by needle aspiration. ● Normal, ▲ Neonatally thymectomised, ——— Macrophage content ------ Malignant tumour cells content

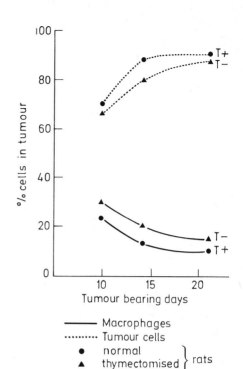

Fig. 2. Macrophage content of non-immunogenic, methylcholanthrene-induced rat sarcoma grown in normal and thymectomised syngeneic Hooded rats. Code as in Fig. 1

underline the important association between the immunogenicity of the tumour, T-cell function and the degree of macrophage infiltration. In T-cell competent animals growing a highly immunogenic tumour there is a marked degree of macrophage infiltration which is effective in localising the tumour. Whereas the non-immunogenic tumour is poorly infiltrated with macrophages and more readily metastasises. In the latter situation T-cell competence does not apparently affect the macrophage host response. However the precise way in which these three different factors are related has yet to be clarified.

## Monocytes in the Rat Leukaemia SAL

In peripheral blood of rats with the SAL leukaemia, there is a population of cells which are glass adherent in the presence of trypsin, bind the specific anti-macrophage serum, are phagocytic and have surface Fc receptors. These cells are still present at the terminal stages of the disease (2-5%). In order to determine their origin, namely to define whether they were derived from the host or the leukaemia, the following experiments were done. The first showed that the monocytosis which occurred during the growth of the SAL leukaemia could be abolished by irradiating the recipient rats with 900r whole body prior dose to giving the SAL cells, which effect could be reserved by reconstituting the animal with normal bone-marrow cells. The second experiment involved the use of August x Marshall $F_1$ hybrids (Fig. 3) in which the SAL leukaemia grew very well, so that the host cells bore Marshall phenotypic surface antigens, which were demonstrated by binding an August anti-Marshall spleen cell serum which had been absorbed, in vivo, in a normal August rat, so that only Marshall transplantation

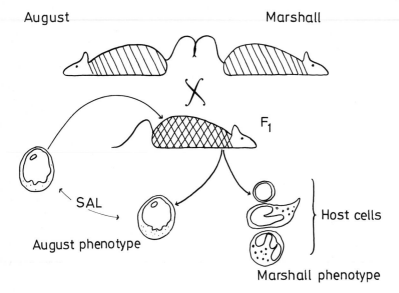

August

Marshall

F₁

SAL

August phenotype

} Host cells

Marshall phenotype

*Fig. 3. Diagram showing growth of August phenotypic transplantated rat myeloid leukemia in F1 hybrids of August x Marshall cross, which produces host cells with Marshall phenotypic surface marker*

antigens were being demonstrated and not cross-reacting auto-antibodies to August surface macromolecules or immune complexes which might bind to Fc receptors. The SAL leukaemic cell itself or course only had August phenotypic surface antigens. The adherent cells from these leukaemic rats were examined and they satisfied the criteria mentioned above for monocytes. 9o-95% of the adherent cells were monocytes and these were shown to have Marshall surface antigens. Finally, the cultured adherent cells grown from the peripheral blood of leukaemic rats were removed by treatment with EDTA and re-injected into normal August rats. These rats did not develop leukaemia.

The pattern of monocytosis (Fig. 4) seen during the growth of the leukaemia in August rats was determined by calculating the percent of adherent cells which bound the anti-macrophage serum during growth, which correlated with the percent of cells in the buffy coat which were AMS positive. In culture the adherent cells did not replicate to any significant degree and their numbers remained relatively stable over a period of several days, unlike the leukaemic cells which died rapidly over a period of 24-48 h of culture. Five days after inoculating August rats with the leukaemia when the leukaemic blast cells were beginning to appear in the peripheral blood in significant numbers, it was noted that the levels of monocytes were also increased. However, on the seventh and eighth day the leukaemic cells increased in number at an accelerated rate, whereas the levels of monocytes began to level off. Other host cells could also be seen in the peripheral blood, these included neutrophils, eosinophils and nucleated red blood cells, which follows the general pattern of the monocyte response. The monocyte function of these leukaemia-bearing rats was tested by evoking a DHS response, in suitably sensitised rats, to injection of PPD into

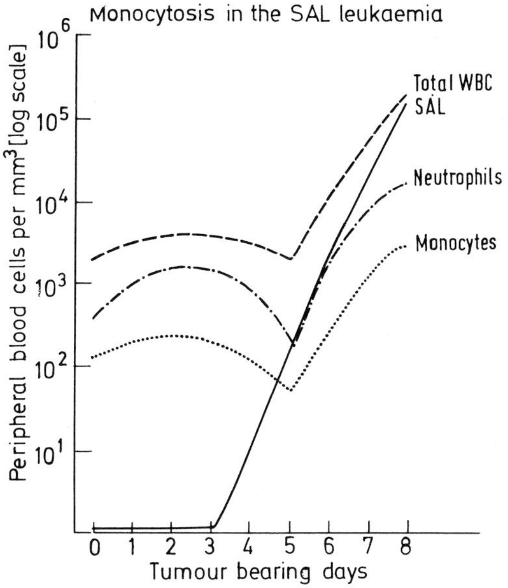

Fig. 4. *Peripheral blood levels of SAL leukaemic blast cells, neutrophils, and monocytes in peripheral blood of normal August rat inoculated with 2 x 10⁵ SAL cells on day 0, by i.v. injection. Monocytes were measured by determining percent of cells in peripheral blood that bound a specific rabbit anti-rat macrophage serum*

the foodpad and measuring the swelling 24 h later and comparing the results in rats that did not have leukaemia. The ability to produce a macrophage-rich inflammatory exudate in response to intra-peritoneal oyster glycogen was also tested. Both these tests of monocyte function were normal in the SAL leukaemia-bearing rats.


## MONOCYTES IN HUMAN ACUTE MYELOGENOUS LEUKAEMIA

Adherent cells were cultured from the peripheral blood of patients with acute myeloblastic and myelo-monocytic leukaemia. They fulfilled the criteria stated for monocytes. Of a group of 15 patients studied, a range of 1-68% adherent monocytoid cells was found, and an analysis of these results would indicate that if less than 5% monocyte adherent cells can be cultured from the peripheral blood of adult patients presenting with acute myelogenous leukaemia, then these patients have considerable difficulty in obtaining a complete remission on the current chemotherapeutic regimens. But the work of BALKWILL and OLIVER more clearly demonstrates this point. Unfortunately it is not possible to repeat the hybridisation experiments in man and therefore definitive proof of the origin of these adherent monocytoid cells from acute leukaemias in man will be a little more difficult to prove. However, whatever their origin, they appear to be directly or indirectly of some importance.


## MACROPHAGE CONTENT OF HUMAN SOLID TUMOURS

Fifty-six human solid tumours have been studied for their macrophage content; 27 breast tumours of which 13 were benign, 19 malignant

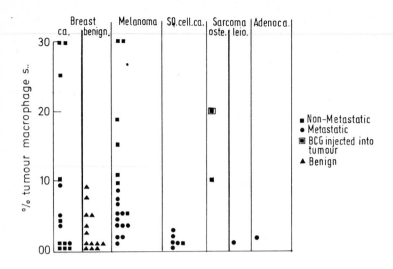

*Fig. 5. Macrophage content of 56 human solid tumours. ■ Non-metastatic,*
*● metastatic, ▣ after BCG injection into the tumour, ▲ benign*

melanomas, 6 squamous cell carcinomas, 2 osteogenic sarcomas, 1 leio-
myosarcoma and 1 adenocarcinoma (Fig. 5). The range of the macrophage
content found was in the range 0-30%. Metastatic tumours have a macrophage content of 9% or less, whereas primary or locally recurrent
tumours have a range of 0-30%. It is too early say whether the primary
tumours with a low macrophage content belong to the group which will
metastasize early; these studies have not been in progress long enough.
The metastatic breast tumours include neoplasms which had invaded
axillary nodes, proven by histology, or skin. Benign breast tumours
have a relatively low macrophage content (less than 10%) and the four
lesions at the upper end of the range may well have been infected.
Widely disseminated secondaries from the same patient, as studied in
some melanomas, were found to have the same degree of macrophage infiltration. One tumour (the osteogenic sarcoma) was studied prior to
and following intra-tumoural BCG injection and an increased macrophage
content was demonstrated following this treatment, though I am not
here advocating this line of therapy!

DISCUSSION

Histogenically similar tumours vary in their inability to evoke a host
response, or perhaps, different hosts vary in their ability to respond
to the same tumour. In solid tumours this is reflected by its macrophage content. Those tumours with a high macrophage content less readily metastasize (1) and this appears to be related to the immunogenicity of the tumour. The macrophage infiltration of a tumour is diminished, in immunogenic tumours, by T-cell depletion (2) and these results confirm this finding. But, even in the normal host bearing an
immunogenic tumour, if T-cell function is diminished, during tumour
growth, either directly or indirectly, perhaps even a result of the
tumour growth itself, then less macrophages will infiltrate it and
possibly allow dissemination. Rats with sarcomas which have a high
macrophage content lose their ability to mount a monocyte response (2)

which we have not found in the SAL leukaemia (6), which is itself a
tumour of low immunogenicity, and is perhaps in line with the finding
that less immunogenic tumours, with lower macrophage infiltrations,
depress monocyte function less (2).

The peripheral blood monocytes in the rat leukaemia are of host origin
and not differentiated leukaemic cells (6). But  this monocytosis is
probably part and partial of non-specific leukoerythroblastic response,
we have no evidence as yet to indicate response specificity. It is
known that colony-stimulating factors are raised in various acute leukaemias (10, 11) perhaps being produced by the leukaemic cells themselves. This might explain the type of picture produced when there is
myelo-stimulation in the presense of a bone marrow increasingly com-
promised by leukaemia. Even so, the presence of "adherent" monocytoid
cells which can be cultured from the peripheral blood of adult human
leukaemias appears to be important in terms of assessing the response
of the disease to chemotherapy. Further studies along these lines
may well prove fruitful.

The preliminary data with regard to the macrophage content of human
solid tumours supports the hypothesis established in rat sarcomas that
the macrophage infiltration of a tumour is an important host response
which localizes the tumor preventing dissemination of the primary
lesion. However, a longer period of study is required before the true
validity of these observations can be tested in man.

It is worthy of mention that the reliability of the techniques used
to measure macrophages and monocytes has rested heavily on the use of
highly specific macrophage surface markers.


SUMMARY

The effective localization of an immunogenic rat sarcoma (HSBPA) is
related to its macrophage content. In order to infiltrate this tumour
with macrophages, T-cell function is important. In a tumour of low
immunogenicity, MC3, with a low macrophage content, thymectomy has
little effect on the ease with which such a tumour metastasizes. The
monocytes in the peripheral blood of a rat myeloid leukaemia are of
host origin and are significantly raised during the growth of the leukaemia. Similar monocytoid cells are found in human acute myelogenous
leukaemias and appear to be important in the prognostic features of
this type of leukaemia. The origin of these monocytoid cells has not
been elucidated. In 56 solid human tumours the macrophage content of
metastatic tumours is low (<10%), whereas the range in primary or
locally recurrent tumours is 0-30%. It is too early to say whether the
low macrophage infiltrated primary will readily metastasize compared
to the high macrophage containing tumour.

ACKNOWLEDGEMENTS

The author was in receipt of a Cancer Research Campaign Fellowship.
Professor Peter Alexander's encouragement and useful advice is warmly
acknowledged. The work with the rat leukaemia model was done in conjunction with Dr. Annette Wrathmell.

REFERENCES

1. Eccles, Suzanne A., Alexander, P.: Macrophage content of tumours
   in relation to metastatic spread and host immune reaction. Nature
   250, 667 (1974)
2. Eccles, Suzanne A., Alexander, P.: Sequestration of macrophages
   in growing tumours and its effect on the immunological capacity of
   the host. Brit. J. Cancer 30, 42 (1974)
3. Evans, R.: Macrophages in syngeneic animal tumours. Transplantation
   14, No. 4, 468 (1972)
4. Gauci, C.L.: Macrophage content of human malignant melanomas.
   Behring Inst. Mitt. 56, 73-78 (1975)
5. Gauci, C.L., Alexander, P.A.: The macrophage content of some human
   tumours. Cancer Letters 1, 29 (1975)
6. Gauci, C.L., Wrathmell, A.B., Alexander, P.: The origin and role
   of blood borne monocytes in rats with a transplanted acute myelogenous leukaemia. Cancer Letters 1, 33 (1975)
7. Gershon, R.K., Carter, R.L., Lane, N.J.: Studies in homotrans-
   plantable lymphomas in hamsters. I. Histologic responses in lymphoid
   tissues and their relationship to metastasis. Amer. J. Pathol.
   49. pp. 637-655 (1966)
8. Gershon, R.K., Carter, R.L., Lane, N.J.: Studies in homotrans-
   plantable lymphomas in hamsters. II. The specificity of the histologic responses in lymphoid tissues and their relationship to
   metastasis. Amer. J. Pathol. 50. pp. 137-157 (1967)
9. Gershon, R.K., Carter, R.L., Lane, N.J.: Studies in homotrans-
   plantable lymphomas in hamsters. IV. Observation on macrophages
   in the expression of tumour immunity. Amer. J. Pathol. 51. pp.
   1111-1125 (1967)
10. Metcalf, D., Moore, M.A.S.: Factors modifying stem cell prolifera-
    tion of myelomonocytic leukaemia cells in vitro and in vivo. J.
    Natl. Cancer Inst. 44, 801 (1970)
11. Moore, M.A.S., Williams, N., Metcalf, D.: In vitro colony formation
    by normal and leukaemic haemopoietic cells: Characterisation of
    the colony forming cells. Internat., J. Cancer 11, 143 (1973)
12. Underwood, J.C.E., Carr, I.: The ultrastructure of the lymphoreti-
    cular cells in non-lymphoid human neoplasms. Virchows Arch. Abt.
    B. Zellpath. 12, 39 (1972)
13. Wrathmell, A.B.: The growth pattern of two transplantable acute
    leukaemias of spontaneous origin in rats. Brit. J. Cancer, 33
    172 (1976)
14. Wrathmell, A., Alexander, P.: V. Immunologic aspects of leukaemia.
    Growth characteristics and immunological properties of a myelo-
    blastic and a lymphoblastic leukaemia in pure line rats. In: Uni-
    fying Concepts of Leukaemia, Bibli. haemat., Dutcher, R.M., Chieco-
    Bianchi L. (eds). Basel: Karger. No. 39, pp. 649-653

# Chapter 17

# Search for Correlations Between Immunological and Morphological Criteria Used to Classify Lymphoid Leukemias and Non-Hodgkin's Hematosarcomas

## with Special Reference to Scanning Electron Microscopy and T and B Membrane Markers

D. BELPOMME, D. DANTCHEV, A. M. KARIMA, N. LELARGE, R. JOSEPH, B. CAILLOU, M. LAFLEUR, and G. MATHÉ

## INTRODUCTION

We have previously published that human leukemias and non-Hodgkin's hematosarcomas can be classified into three distinct categories of diseases by using T and B lymphocytes membrane markers (3, 5, 6). The first group is devoted to T-cell diseases, the second to B-cell neoplasia, while the third is composed of disorders related to null cell disease because neoplastic cells of this category lack detectable membrane markers of both T- and B-lymphocytes.

Recently a classification of leukemias and non-Hodgkin's hematosarcomas, mainly based on cytology and histology, has been established by the WHO (11).

It is the object of this paper (a) to report on the different morphological as well as immunological investigations used to classify leukemias and non-Hodgkin's hematosarcomas, and (b) to search for the existence of a correlation between the results obtained with the different methods in a attempt to present a unified classification of these neoplasia based on objective criteria.

In this study, cell typing of neoplastic diseases includes not only conventional morphological methods such as cytology and histology (12) but scanning electron microscopy (9), in addition to a battery of immunological tests used for the detection of a T or B membrane markers (1).

## MATERIAL AND METHODS

### 1. Cytohistological Diagnosis of Disorders

Eighty-nine cases of chronic and acute mononuclear cell disorders including 26 cases of chronic lymphoid leukemias (CLL), 30 cases of typical acute lymphoid leukemias (ALL) and 33 cases of non-Hodgkin's hematosarcomas were investigated.

Non-Hodgkin's hematosarcomas including 31 cases of leukaemic lymphosarcomas (LS), and two cases of so-called reticulosarcomas (RS) were in addition examined.

All these proliferative disorders have been classified by using the
WHO nomenclature (11). The diagnosis has been made on May-Grünwald-
Giemsa stained  bone-marrow smears in the case of leukemia, and on
hematin-eosin stained sections in the case of non-Hodgkin's hematosarcomas. Reticulosarcomas have been distinguished from lymphosarcomas
by the presence of large blastic nucleated cells in imprints and by
the presence of pericellular reticulin fibrils in sections.

Lymphosarcomas have been classified into nodular and diffuse varieties
on section (20).


## 2. Cytological Subclassification of the Disorders

Subclassification of ALL and LS has been achieved according to the WHO
classification by carefully analyzing the May-Grünwald-Giemsa stained
bone-marrow smears and/or lymph-node imprints in complement of sections.

Typical ALL has been divided into prolymphoblastic (Pro LB), macrolymphoblastic (Ma LB), microlymphoblastic (Mi LB), and prolymphocytic
(Pro LC) types; immunoblastic ALL have been the object of other reports
(5, 16). Nonleukemic as well as leukemic LS have been classified into
prolymphocytic (Pro LC), lymphoblastic (or lymphoblastoid) (LB), and
immunoblastic (I) varieties, according to the subclassification of these
diseases originally proposed by our group (13, 14, 15, 16).
Chronic lymphoid leukemias (CLL) have been divided into 3 groups according to morphological criteria: Group I is devoted to CLL composed
of small differentiated lymphocytes (7-10 µ diameter), while group II
concerns CLL composed of cells of mixed type including nucleated lymphocytes of small or intermediate size (10-15 µ diameter). Group III
corresponds to CLL composed of large nucleated lymphocytes (15-20 µ)
(Table 3).


## 3. Scanning Electron Microscopy (SEM)

SEM of neoplastic cells from lymph-node biopsies and/or bone marrow
and/or peripheral blood has been performed in 37 cases according to the
critical point-drying method (18). Results of this investigation have
allowed us to classify mononuclear neoplastic cell surface appearances
into four main categories:

Type 1 is devoted to completely smooth-surfaced cells, type 2 to smooth
undulated cells, while type 3 concerns villous cells having less than
30 short microvilli per exposed surface and type 4, "villous" cells
with more than 30 microvilli per exposed surface (Table 1), (Fig. 1)
(9).


Table 1. Classification of cell-surface appearance according to SEM

| Type | 1 | 2 | 3 | 4 |
|------|---|---|---|---|
| Appearance | Completely smooth | Smooth ondulated | Partially villous | Completely villous |
| Villosities Number | O | O | < 30 | > 30 |

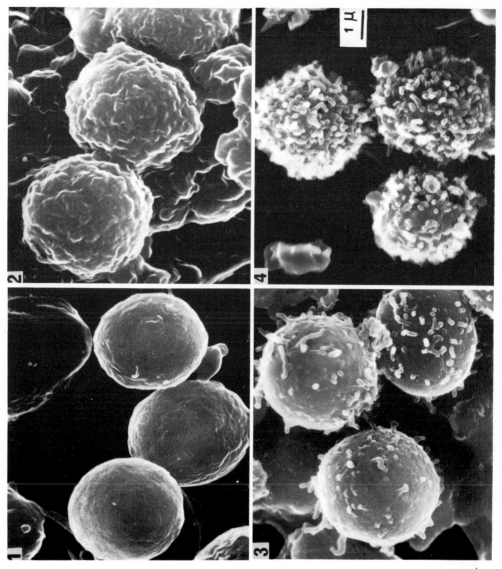

Fig. 1. Surface of different
lymphoid leukemia and hematosarcoma cells in SEM: Type 1:
completely smooth surface;
Type 2: undulated surface;
Type 3: a few short microvilli; Type 4: numerous microvilli, so-called villous
lymphocytes

## 4. Immunological Test Procedures

Table 2 summarizes the immunologic cell-membrane markers of normal T- and B-lymphocytes and monocytes (1, 21), and the different tests used in this study to characterize neoplastic cells. Details of methods have been previously reported (1). Search for correlation between morphological and immunological tests has been achieved by the double-bind method.

Table 2. Immunological cell membrane markers

| Investigations | Markers | Results T | B | Monocytes |
|---|---|---|---|---|
| E rosettes[a] | E | + | O | O |
| EA rosettes[b] | FcAgAc | (+) ? | (+) ? | + |
| EAC rosettes[c] | $C_3'$ | O | + | + |
| Membrane immunofluorescence | mIg[d] | O | + | O |

| | |
|---|---|
| FcAgAc | = Fc receptors for antigen-antibody complexes |
| $C_3'$ | = Activated $C_3'$ complement receptors |
| mIg | = Membrane immunoglobulins (synthetized by cells) |
| SIg | = Surface immunoglobulins (adsorbed on cells) |
| ( ) | = On some mononuclear cells |

[a] Spontaneous rosettes with sheep red blood cells (SRBC).
[b] Rosettes with red blood cells (RBC) sensitized by anti-RBC antibodies.
[c] Rosettes with RBC sensitized by anti-RBC antibodies in the presense of complement.
[d] Are distinguished from SIg by testing cells after in vitro incubation for 6 h.


## RESULTS

### 1. Chronic Lymphoid Leukemias (CLL)

1.1. Cytological Data. Nine out of the 26 cases studied were classified in the cytological group I, 14 in group II, and three in group III (Table 3)

1.2. Scanning Electron Microscopy (SEM). Six out of the eight cases studied with SEM, whatever their cytological type, presented cells with a villous surface appearance. Five of these cases were classified as type 4 and the others as type 3 (Table 4). Differences in length and number of villosities have, however, been encountered when comparing cells in a given case, as well as when comparing different cases. Two other cases were classified as smooth undulated (type 2).

1.3. Immunological Data. Twenty-two out of 26 cases studied were characterized by a monoclonal proliferation of B-lymphocytes, while in four cases there were no detectable B cell membrane markers. In fact, two of these latter cases were thought to be T-cell derived, because of high number of E-rosette-forming lymphocytes with sheep red blood cells (SRBC), while the two others could not be typed because of lack of detectable T or B membrane markers (Table 3).

Table 3. Cell membrane markers according to cell typing in CLL (26 cases)

| Immunological type Cytological type | Number of cases | B | Non-B |
|---|---|---|---|
| Group I[a] | 9 | 7 | 2 |
| Group II[b] | 14 | 13 | 1 |
| Group III[c] | 3 | 2 | 1 |
| Total | 26 | 22 | 4[d] |

[a] Small lymphocytes (7-10 μ diameter)
[b] Mixed type with sometimes nucleolated lymphocytes of small or intermediate size (10-15 μ diameter)
[c] Large sometimes nucleolated lymphocytes (15-10 μ diameter)
[d] Including 2 so-called T-cell CLL

Table 4. Cell membrane markers and SEM in CLL (8 cases)

| SEM Immunological cell typing | Type 1 | Type 2 | Type 3 | Type 4 | Total |
|---|---|---|---|---|---|
| B | 0/8 | 0/8 | 1/8 | 5/8 | 6/8 |
| Non-B | 0/8 | 2[a]/8 | 0/8 | 0/8 | 2/8 |
| Total | 0/8 | 2/8 | 1/8 | 5/8 | 8/8 |

[a] One case is a so-called T-cell CLL, and the other case is characterized by cells with no detectable T and B cell membrane markers.

1.4. Search for Correlations. All the B-cell CLL studied with SEM presented cells with numerous membrane villosities, (type 4), whatever has been observed cytological types of CLL (Table 4). There was, however, a great variation in the degree of villosity. In two non-B-cell CLL, including one case of so-called T-cell CLL, the majority of cells found to possess relatively smooth undulated surfaces, and thus to correspond to type 2 of the proposed morphological classification of diseases based on SEM.

## 2. Typical Acute Lymphoid Leukemias (ALL)

2.1. Cytological Data. Table 5 summarizes our results. Eight of the 30 cases studied were of the prolymphocytic type, four of the microlymphoblastic type, seven of the macrolymphoblastic type, while 11 were of the prolymphoblastic type.

Table 5. Cell membrane markers in primary conventional ALL (30 patients)

| Immunological type<br><br>Cytological type | Number of cases | T | B | NDMM[a] |
|---|---|---|---|---|
| Prolymphocytic | 8 | 4/8 | 0/8 | 4/8 |
| Microlymphoblastic | 4 | 0/4 | 0/4 | 3/4 |
| Macrolymphoblastic | 7 | 3/7 | 0/7 | 5/7 |
| Prolymphoblastic | 11 | 0/11 | 0/11 | 11/11 |
| Total | 30 | 7 | 0 | 23 |

[a] No detectable membrane markers.

2.2. Scanning Electron Microscopy (SEM). In all nine cases studied, leukemic cells appeared to be relatively smooth-surfaced. Seven cases were classified as smooth undulated (type 2) and the two others as completely smooth (type 1). There were, however, in several cases of this series a few cells associated with a slight degree of villosity.

2.3. Immunological Data. The results are presented in Table 5. Seven out of the 30 cases studied have been classified as T-cell ALL, because of the detection of E-rosette-forming leukemic cells with SRBC, and because of the lack of B cell membrane markers.

In contast, the 23 remaining cases could not be typed as T- or B-cell diseases because of the absence of T and B membrane markers on the leukemic cells.

2.4. Search for Correlations. Four out of seven T-cell ALL cases were of the prolymphocytic type, three of macrolymphoblastic. There were no T-cell cases both in the group of prolymphoblastic neither microlymphoblastic ALL, while four out of eight cases of prolymphoblastic ALL were of the T type.

All the three T-cell cases studied with SEM showed a cell surface having relatively smooth undulated appearance (type 2), and similar results were obtained in six cases of so-called null-cell ALL. Four cases were classified as type 2 and two as type 1 (Table 6).

## 3. Non-Hodgkin's Hematosarcomas

3.1. Reticulosarcomas. The 2 cases of diffuse non-Hodgkin's hematosarcomas classified as reticulosarcomas were characterized by absence of T and B detectable markers. In one case studied so far, SEM showed that the cell surfaces had a completely smooth appearance (Table 7).

Table 6. Cell membrane markers and SEM in typical ALL (9 cases)

| SEM<br>Immunological<br>cell typing | Type 1 | Type 2 | Type 3 | Type 4 | Total |
|---|---|---|---|---|---|
| T | 0/9 | 3[a]/9 | 0/9 | 0/9 | 3/9 |
| NDMM | 2[b]/9 | 4[c]/9 | 0/9 | 0/9 | 6/9 |
| Total | 2/9 | 7/9 | 0/9 | 0/9 | 9/9 |

[a] One case of macrolymphoblastic type, 2 cases of prolymphocytic type.
[b] Two cases of prolymphoblastic type.
[c] One case of prolymphocytic type, two of macrolymphoblastic type and one of prolymphoblastic type.

Table 7. Cell membrane markers in RS

| No. of cases | T | B | NDMM[a] |
|---|---|---|---|
| 2 | 0/2 | 0/2 | 2/2 |

[a] No detectable membrane markers.


3.2. Lymphosarcomas. 3.2.1. Cytological and Histological Data. Table 8 and 9 summarize our results: There were 6 cases classified as immunoblastic, 9 as lymphoblastic (or lymphoblastoid), and 16 as prolymphocytic. Six cases were histologically classified as nodular, and 16 as diffuse. Nineteen cases including three of the nodular and seven of the diffuse previous cases, were associated with a leukemic conversion. In nine of 19 cases, there were no available lymph-node biopsies because of early leukemic conversion (Table 8).


Table 8. Cell membrane markers in prolymphocytic, lymphoblastic, and immunoblastic lymphosarcomas (31 patients)

| Cytological type | Number of cases | T | B | NDMM[c] |
|---|---|---|---|---|
| Prolymphocytic lymphosarcoma | 16 | 2[a]/16 | 12/16 | 2[b]/16 |
| Lymphoblastic (lymphoblastoid) lymphosarcoma | 9 | 1/9 | 3/9 | 5/9 |
| Immunoblastic lymphosarcoma | 6 | 2[b] | 3 | 1 |
| Total | 31 | 5 | 18 | 8 |

[a] With mediastinal mass.
[b] One with mediastinal mass.
[c] No detectable membrane markers.

Table 9. Cell membrane markers according to histological typing in lymphosarcomas

| Histological type | Number of cases | T | B | NDMM[d] |
|---|---|---|---|---|
| Nodular | 6[a]/31 | 0/6 | 5/6 | 1/6 |
| Diffuse | 16[b]/31 | 3/16 | 8/16 | 5/16 |
| Early leukemic conversion | 9[c]/31 | 2/9 | 5/9 | 2/9 |
| Total | 31/31 | 5/31 | 18/31 | 8/31 |

[a] Three cases.

[b] Seven cases.

[c] No lymph-node.

[d] No detectable membrane markers.

3.3. Scanning Electron Microscopy. The results are presented in Table 10. Four out of 19 cases studied with SEM were classified as type 1, six as type 2, eight as type 3, and two as type 4 (Fig. 1).

3.4. Immunological Data. Table 8 summarizes our results. Five out of 31 cases studied have been classified as T, and 18 as B. In eight cases there were no detectable T and B membrane markers on the neoplastic cells.

3.5. Search for Correlations. The 18 B-cell cases include five out of six nodular and 13 of 25 diffuse and/or leukemic LS studied.

All nodular LS were cytologically typed as prolymphocytic while the 13 diffuse B-cell LS include a majority of prolymphocytic LS (seven cases), but also three immunoblastic and three lymphoblastic (lymphoblastoid) LS.

SEM showed that in all prolymphocytic LS, except one, neoplastic cells were associated with a villous surface appearance, of type 3 or 4. Similar findings were obtained in one case of B immunoblastic and one case of B lymphoblastic LS studied so far.

In contrast, to these B-cell LS, which were for the most part of the prolymphocytic type, the eight so-called null-cell LS have been found to include a majority of lymphoblastic LS (five cases) in addition to one case of immunoblastic and two cases of prolymphocytic LS.

SEM of four lymphoblastic LS revealed that neoplastic cells were associated with relatively smooth surfaces (type 1 or 2) whereas they were found to be villous in one case of prolymphocytic LS (type 3).

Finally five cases including two immunoblastic, one lymphoblastic (lymphoblastoid), and two prolymphocytic LS were classified as T-cell disorders. SEM showed that in all cases studied, neoplastic cells were smooth-surfaced, whatever their cytological variety.

Table 10. Cell membrane markers, SEM and cytology in LS (19 cases)

| SEM Immunological cell typing | Type 1 | Type 2 | Type 3 | Type 4 | Total |
|---|---|---|---|---|---|
| T | 1/19 (Pro Lc 1/19) | 3/19 (LB 2/19) (I 1/19) | 0/19 | 0/19 | 4/19 |
| B | 0/19 | 1/19 (Pro Lc 1/19) | 7/19 (Pro Lc 5/19) (Lb 1/19) (I 1/19) | 2/19 (Pro Lc 2/19) | 10/19 |
| NDMM[a] | 2/19 (Lb 2/19) | 2/19 (Lb 2/19) | 1/19 (Pro Lc 1/19) | 0/19 | 5/19 |
| Total | 3/19 | 6/19 | 8/19 | 2/19 | 19/19 |

[a] No detectable membrane markers.

Pro Lc = prolymphocytic.

Lb   = lymphoblastic (or lymphoblastoid).

I    = immunoblastic.

## DISCUSSION

The availability of morphological as well as immunological tests for distinguishing human T- and B-lymphocytes and monocytes has led to efforts to classify hematological neoplasia.

Our investigation attempts to reduce the existing confusion in this area by applying strict diagnosis criteria including morphological as well as immunological methods.

In typical CLL, we have confirmed that the majority of cases are mono-clonal B type (3, 19, 21) and have shown that this immunological char-acteristic could not, in fact, be correlated with the cytological classification of CLL, since these B-cell cases include all the three cytological types. Our study showed that there is a good correlation between SEM cell surfaces and cell membrane immunologic phenotypes, since all B-cell cases are composed of villous-surfaced neoplastic cells, whereas non-B CLL, including one case of so-called T-cell CLL, are associated with a relatively smooth-surfaced appearance.

In typical ALL, we confirmed our preliminary reports (1, 2) showing that about 25% of typical ALL are T type, while the remaining cases are classified as so-called null-cell leukemias (1, 3, 7, 8).

In contrast to others, we did not find any cases of primary ALL asso-ciated with B cell membrane markers. We have postulated that this discrepancy may result from a confusion between primary ALL and early leukemic lymphosarcomas (3, 5).

An interesting observation is the predominance of prolymphocytic leu-kemias in the group of T cell ALL (4/7), while all prolymphoblastic leukemias are included in the group of null-cell leukemias.

We have previously discussed the significance of null-cell disorders, with special reference to indifferentiated, i.e., prolymphoblastic leu-kemias (6).

Our findings suggest a possible correlation between the degree of cyto-logical cell differentiation and the presence or absence of T membrane markers. This observation, however, needs further evaluation, since: (a) there are three macrolymphoblastic ALL in the group of T-cell leuke-mias, and (b) our series of T-cell leukemias still remains limited. Furthermore, such a correlation between cytological appearances and immunological membrane phenotypes of leukemic cells has not been established in recent reports (17), but the cytological criteria used to classify ALL differed from those of our study. Using SEM, we showed that the leukemic cells of either T- or so-called null-cell ALL, were in fact smooth-surfaced, whatever their cytological type.

This preliminary data suggest that there is a good correlation between SEM leukemic cell surface appearance and absence of detectable B membrane markers but SEM does not permit identification of T-cell ALL from so-called null-cell All, a finding which has also been observed in LS.

In LS, we found that the majority of B-cell cases were prolymphocytic type, and that these cases were often composed of villous cells. In addition, we confirmed that the great majority of nodular LS was included in this group (10). In contrast, T-cell, as well as so-called null-cell LS, have most often been found to be lymphoblastic (or lymphoblastoid) type, and cells of the majority of such cases have been shown to be smooth-surfaced. These findings suggest (a) that in LS there is, in the majority of cases, a good correlation between results, obtained from cytology, SEM, and immunological investigations, and (b) that as in ALL, T-cell LS could not be morphologically distinguished from null-cell LS, a result suggesting that at least some null-cell LS may be T-cell disorders lacking T markers.

These observations, however, need further evaluation since, as previously discussed (4), the group of so-called null-cell disorders (a) may cover different physiopathological entities and since (b) our different immunological group of LS as well as ALL are not cytologically homogenous.

Furthermore, immunoblastic LS have been found to be B in three cases, T in two, and "null" in one (Table 8).

Finally, our data suggest several points: while T-cell ALL are often associated with a prolymphocytic type, prolymphocytic LS are, in contrast, often associated with B-cell membrane markers.

In contrast to these T- or B-cell cases, so-called null cell disorders, including ALL as well as LS and RS have been found to be associated with a relatively less differentiated cytological pattern suggesting a lack (or a loss) of immunologic membrane markers related to cell differentiation.

SEM of these null cases showed a relatively smooth cell surface appearance, a finding which has, however, also been observed in all cases of T-cell leukemias and LS in our series. In contrast, in the majority of B-cell disorders studied, cells were found to be associated with villous surface appearance.

Although, in a great number of cases, SEM provides a means of distinguishing B-cell diseases from the other disorders, in a few cases this distinction was not clearly correlated with the immunological findings. Whether or not this discrepancy may result from technical problems which are still encountered in both techniques (5, 9, 18), or correspond to modifications of cell-membrane properties related to functional or cell-cycle-dependent variations remains a matter of speculation.

It is evident that the value of the different morphological, as well as immunological methods used in this study still remains questionable and that each test still needs a critical evaluation as previously discussed. From the information we have already gathered, we believe however that it is through the use of such extended investigations, correlated with the clinical evaluation of the diseases, that progress will be made toward improved classification of leukemias and non-Hodgkin's hematosarcomas. Than supported by grants from INSERM ATP 10743 objective cirteria will soon replace our traditional concepts with the final aim of improving the physiopathological understanding of the diseases as well as standardizing therapeutic indications.

REFERENCES

1. Belpomme, D., Dantchev, D., Du Rusquec, E., Grandjon, D., Huchet, R., Pouillart, P., Schwarzenberg, L., Amiel, J., Mathé, G.: T and B lymphocyte markers on the neoplastic cell of 20 patients with chronic lymphoid leukemia. Biomed. 20, 109 (1974)

2. Belpomme, D., Dantchev, D., Du Rusquec, E., Grandjon, D., Huchet, R., Pinon, F., Pouillart, P., Schwarzenberg, L., Amiel, J.L., Mathé, G.: La nature T ou B des cellules neoplastiques des leucémies lymphöides. Bulletin du Cancer 61, 387 (1974)

3. Belpomme, D., Dantchev, D., Joseph, R., Mathé, G.: Further studies of acute and chronic leukemias T and B cells surface markers and scanning electron microscopy. Excerpta Medica 1, 143 (1975)

4. Belpomme, D., Dantchev, D., Joseph, R., Santoro, A., Lelarge, N., Feuilhade De Chauvin, F., Grandjon, D., Mathé, G.: Cell membrane markers of T and B lymphocytes and monocytes in leukemias and hematosarcomas. Excerpta Medica 39, 298 (1975)

5. Belpomme, D., Dantchev, D., Joseph, R., Santoro, A., Feuilhade De Chauvin, F., Lelarge, N., Grandjon, D., Pontvert, D., Mathé, G.: Classification of leukemias and hematosarcomas based on cell membrane markers and scanning electron microscopy. Europ. J. Cancer 1, 131 (1976)

6. Belpomme, D., Lelarge, D., Feuilhade De Chauvin, F., Joseph, R., Mathé, G.: An immunological classification of leukemias and hematosarcomas based on cell membrane markers with special reference to null cell disorders. This volume, pp. 98

7. Borella, L., Sen, L.: Cell surface markers on lymphoblasts from acute lymphocytic leukemia. J. Immunol. 111, 1257 (1973)

8. Brouet, J.C., Toben, T.R., Chevalier, A., Seligman, M.: T and B membrane markers on blast cells in 69 patients with acute lymphoblastic leukemia. Ann. Immunol. (Inst. Past.) 125C, 691 (1974)

9. Dantchev, D.: Revised semiolgy of the different mononuclear cells under scanning electron microscopy. This volume, pp. 8-16

10. Jaffe, E.S., Shevach, E.M., Frank, M.M., Berard, C.W., Green, I.: Nodular lymphoma evidence for origin from follicular B lymphocytes. New Engl. J. Med. 290, 813 (1974)

11. Mathé, G., Rappaport, H.: Histological and cytological typing of the neoplastic diseases of the hematopoietic and lymphoid tissues, Vol. 1. Geneva: W.H.O. (1976)

12. Mathé, G., Seman, G.: Aspects histologiques et cytologiques des leucémies et hématosarcomes, Vol. 1. Librairie Maloine S.A. (1963)

13. Mathé, G., Pouillart, P., Sterescu, M., Amiel, J.L., Schwarzenberg, L., Schneider, M., Hayat, M., De Vassal, F., Jasmin, C., Lafleur, M.: Subdivision of classical varieties of acute leukemias. Correlation with prognosis and cure expectancy. Europ. J. Clin. Biol. Res. 16, 554 (1971)

14. Mathé, G., Pouillart, P., Schwarzenberg, L., Amiel, J.L., Schneider, M., Hayat, H., De Vassal, F., Jasmin, C., Rosenfeld, C., Weiner, R., Rappaport, H.: Attempts at immunotherapy of 100 patients with acute lymphoid leukemia: some factors influencing results. Nat. Cancer Inst. Mon. 35, 361 (1972)

15. Mathé, G., Pouillart, P., Weiner, R., Hayat, M., Sterescu, M., Lafleur, M.: Classification and sub-classification of acute leukemias correlated with clinical expression, therapeutic sensitivity and prognosis. Recent Results in Cancer Research 43, 6 (1973)

16. Mathé, G., Belpomme, D., Dantchev, D., Pouillart, P., Jasmin, C., Misset, J.L., Musset, M., Amiel, J.L., Schlumberger, J.R., Schwarzenberg, L., Hayat, M., De Vassal, F., Lafleur, M.: Immunoblastic acute lymphoid leukemia. Biomed. 20, 333 (1974)

17. Murphy, S.M., Borella, L., Sen, L., Mauer, A.: Lack of correlation of lymphoblast cell size with presence of T-cell markers or with outcome in childhood acute lymphoblastic leukemia. Brit. J. Haematol. 31, 95 (1975)

18. Polliack, A., Lampen, N., Clarkson, B.D., De Harven, E., Bentwich, Z., Siegal, F.P., Kunkel, H.G.: Identification of human B and T lymphocytes by scanning electrom microscopy. J. Exper. Med. 138, 607 (1973)

19. Preud'Homme, J.L., Seligman, M.: Surface bound immunoglobulins as cell markers im human proliferative diseases. Blood <u>40</u>, 777 (1972)
20. Rappaport, H.: Tumor of the hematopoietic system. Armed Forces Institut of Pathology, Washington D.C. (1966). Vol. 1
21. Seligman, M., Preud'Homme, J.L., Brouet, J.C.: B and T cell markers in human proliferative blood diseases and primary immuno-deficiencies, with special reference to membrane bound immunoglobulins. Transpl. Rev. <u>16</u>, 85 (1973)

# Chapter 18

# Non-Hodgkin's Hematosarcoma ("Lymphomas"): Classification of the W. H. O. Reference Center for Neoplastic Disease of Hemopoietic and Lymphoid Tissues

G. MATHÉ and D. DANTCHEV

Non-Hodgkin's hematosarcomas are tumors of the lymphoid cells (lympho-sarcomas) or the "reticulo-endothelial system" cells (reticulosarcomas) which, contrary to leukemias, are initially localized or circumscribed. This characteristic, although important, does not separate hemato-sarcomas sharply from leukemias, as hematosarcomas may secondarily present a systemic dissemination and the lymphosarcomas may convert into lymphoid leukemias.

## GENERALITIES

The successes achieved in recent years by the rational treatment of Hodgkin's disease (see review in ref. 21) have temporarily cast the non-Hodgkin's hematosarcomas, lymphosarcomas, and reticulosarcomas (LRS) into the shade.

But interest in these neoplasias has been renewed: (a) in connection with their histological and cytological classification, a classification that the W.H.O. asked one of us to study when he was placed in charge of the Leukemia and Hematosarcoma Reference Center (19); (b) in con-nection with another classification according to the immunological markers of their cells (6, 8, 9, 12, 13, 16, 26), and (c) in connection with the development of medical treatments, which are now as effective on these tumors as on Hodgkin's disease (11, 16, 18, 22).

## 1. THE LYMPHOCYTES AND THE MACROPHAGE MONONUCLEAR CELL SYSTEM

Cells that cause non-Hodgkin's hematosarcomas belong either to the lymphocyte family or to the "reticular-endothelial system." The latter is common to lymphoid tissues, bone marrow, and several other types of tissue such as skin (1).

### 1.1. The Lymphocyte Line

The lymphocyte line was formerly thought to be descended from stem cells that morphologists called "lymphoblasts", located in lymphoid tissue; on the other hand, more differentiated components of this line, lymphocytes, were supposed to share their life between the lymphoid tissue, the blood, and the lymphatic vessels.

Although, we know today that lymphocyte stem cells are located in the
bone marrow, it is not known whether they correspond to what cyto-
morphologists call "lymphoblasts." They probably differ in appearance,
depending on whether they are in the cell division cycle or quiescent.
It is not known whether the cells leaving the bone marrow are more
differentiated lymphocytes and come from prolymphocytes, i.e., cells
which are intermediate between lymphoblasts and lymphocytes. Although
lymphocytes are apparently differentiated cells, it is also not known
whether they take on the aspects of what morphologists have, for a
long time, called "lymphoblasts," when they divide, but it is not an
unreasonable hypothesis.

Some lymphocytic cells leaving the marrow, and referred to as B cells
(B = bone marrow), are specifically responsible for humoral mediated
immunity, which works through antibodies produced by the plasmocytes.
These B cells themselves become plasmocytes after first being transformed into intermediary cells known as B-immunoblasts. Whereas lymphocytes and plasmocytes do not split up, immunoblasts proliferate very
rapidly and some of them revert to a type known as B-memory lymphocytes.

Other (T) lymphocytic cells leave the bone marrow for the thymus,
where they receive a message that enables them to perform functions
indispensable to cellular mediated immunity. When cells with this capacity leave the thymus, they are generally called T-pos-thymus-lympho-
cytes. When they come into contact with the antigen, they turn into
T-immunoblasts which proliferate rapidly and are capable of several
functions: they can kill live antigen carriers, release soluble factors
capable of on-the-spot macrophage immobilization (MIF = macrophage
inhibiting factor), of macrophage activation (MAF = macrophage activating factor) or, finally, of ending up as T-memory lymphocytes.

For a large number of antigens, antibody production calls for cooperation between B-lymphocytes and what are known as helper T-lymphocytes.

It is important to note that evidence has been produced, in the case
of the lymph nodes and spleen, of the existence of histological T-
lymphocyte sites (paracortical areas of the lymph nodes and periarte-
riolar areas of the spleen) and B-lymphocyte sites respectively
(germinal centers and medullary area of the lymph nodes) (29).


1.2. The Mononuclear Macrophage System

The mononuclear macrophage system, as it has been called since the
release of a recent WHO study (VAN FURTH et al., 1972), is none other
than Aschoff's reticulo-endothelial system (1). In particular, Aschoff
discerned the following types of cell: reticular, in the case of the
spleen and lymph nodes, reticulo-endothelial in blood and lymphatic
sinusus, histiocytes and monocytes. W.H.O. nomenclature refers to
"fixed and free macrophages" and "conjunctive tissue histiocytes" (31).

Progress in this field does not in reality consist of eliminating the
term "reticular cell," which anglo-american authors dislike, and
replacing it with "fixed macrophages", but in the work of VAN FURTH
et al. (30, 32) and VOLKMAN and GOWANS (34), who evolved a more or less
valid conception of the origins and linear development of the different
cell types, as shown in Figure 1 (31).

We shall use Aschoff's term "reticular cells" to denote cells surrounding themselves with the reticulin they produce, rather than the
term "macrophage", which can give rise to serious confusion as regards
the cell's functional state, since a macrophage in the WHO sense may
or may not be in a macrophagic state.

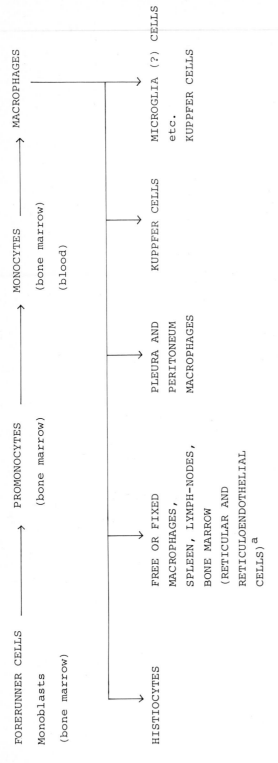

FORERUNNER CELLS $\longrightarrow$ PROMONOCYTES $\longrightarrow$ MONOCYTES $\longrightarrow$ MACROPHAGES

Monoblasts

(bone marrow)                (bone marrow)      (bone marrow)

                                               (blood)

HISTIOCYTES        FREE OR FIXED        PLEURA AND        KUPPFER CELLS        MICROGLIA (?) CELLS
                   MACROPHAGES,         PERITONEUM                             etc.
                   SPLEEN, LYMPH-NODES, MACROPHAGES                            KUPPFER CELLS
                   BONE MARROW
                   (RETICULAR AND
                   RETICULOENDOTHELIAL
                   CELLS)[a]

*Fig. 1. Mononuclear macrophage system (31)*

[a] Certain authors (36) think reticular cells may not come from monocytes but could belong to a strain
of fibroblasts or intermediate forerunner cells, of a type somewhere between hematopoietic stem
cells and fibroblasts.

# 2. HISTOLOGICAL AND CYTOLOGICAL TYPING (TABLE 1)

Lympho- and reticulosarcomas differ from Hodgkin's disease in that their neoplasms contain no "inflammatory" cells. In Hodgkin's disease, such agents take up a considerable part of the tumor, and their proportion and typing, according to appearance, determine the prognosis (see review in ref. 11).

This group of diseases as a whole represents what Virchow initially described in 1863 under the heading lymphosarcoma (LS). Within this group, OBERLING (23) individualized the reticulosarcoma (RS) in 1928, defining it as a tumor of "reticular-endothelial" cells which he distinguished from lymphosarcoma in the strict sense, the latter being neoplastic cells of the lymphocyte family. In 1925, BRILL et al. (3), followed by SYMMERS (28) in 1927, finally individualized a type which, under the microscope, appeared to be nodular in shape. In 1970, BURKITT and WRIGHT (4) succeeded in isolating an African histologically diffuse variety, the tissue of which, consisting of lymphoid cells, is permeated by macrophages which give sections a "starry sky" appearance.

Regardless of the work done on the classification of non-Hodgkin's hematosarcomas (an account of this work can be found in MATHE and SEMAN (20), and by RAPPAPORT (25), and in recent articles by MATHE et al. (13), LUKES and COLLINS (9), and LENNERT et al. (8)), there is no scientific reason whatever for abandoning the terminology traditionally used to designate the chief neoplastic groups of lymphocytes and mononuclear macrophages, which we chose for the WHO classification (19). This moreover remains true despite the impossibility of combining the six classifications - proposed by RAPPAPORT, LUKES, LENNERT, DORFMAN, BENNETT, and MATHE (35), respectively - into a single category.

In line with this classification, the histopathologist can distinguish the following types of tumors under a weak magnifying lens: (a) nodular lymphosarcomas (Figs. 2 and 3); (b) diffused lymphosarcomas (Fig. 4); recent findings have led to two special types being classified under this heading, Burkitt's lymphosarcoma (Fig. 5) and mycosis fungoides (Fig. 6); and (c) reticulosarcoma, easily identifiable by its dense reticulin fiber network (Fig. 7).

Histological examination under a powerful lens of sections, as well as their cytological examination on smears or imprints, enable several known or new types to be recognized among the nodular and diffused varieties of LS, and also help to identify RS.

2.1. Three parameters are available for typing nodular lymphosarcoma: the prolymphocytic or lymphoblastic (or lymphoblastoid) appearance of the cells on sections and smears (13), the large number of cells with cleaved nuclei visible on smears (13) (Plate I.1) and sections (9) (Fig. 8), and the size of the cells. The best way is to describe the three parameters for each case; there are mainly two types: (a) one in which prolymphocytes, cleaved nucleus cells and small cells predominate (Fig. 8) (Plate I.1), and (b) one in which there is a greater proportion of lymphoblasts and of cells with uncleaved nuclei or large cells: this type will be referred to as prolymphocytic-lymphoblastic, dominated by cells with uncleaved nuclei or dominated by large or mixed cells (Fig. 9).

2.2. In diffuse lymphosarcomas there are even more different types, as follows:

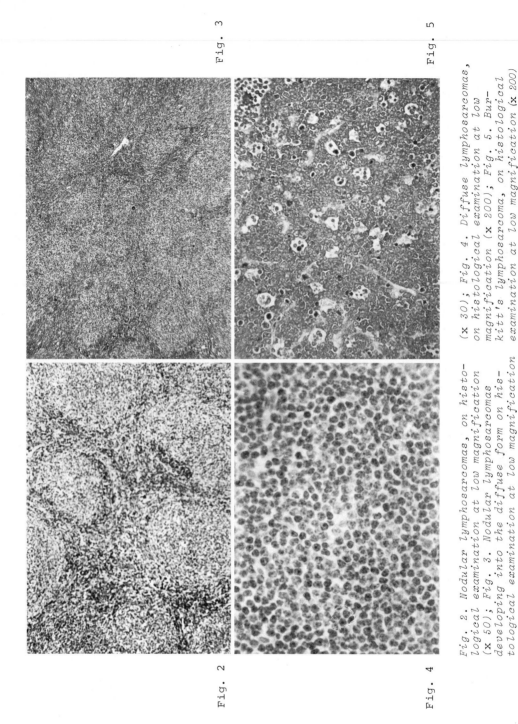

Fig. 3

Fig. 5

Fig. 2

Fig. 4

*Fig. 2. Nodular lymphosarcomas, on histological examination at low magnification (x 50); Fig. 3. Nodular lymphosarcomas developing into the diffuse form on histological examination at low magnification* (x 30); *Fig. 4. Diffuse lymphosarcomas, on histological examination at low magnification (x 200); Fig. 5. Burkitt's lymphosarcoma, on histological examination at low magnification (x 200)*

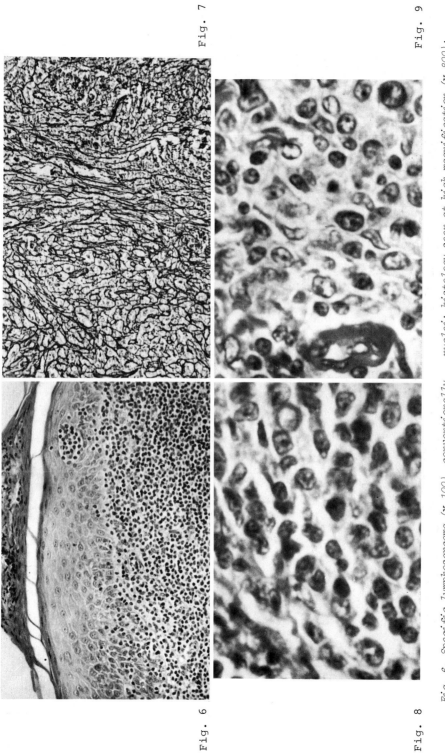

Fig. 6

Fig. 7

Fig. 8

Fig. 9

*Fig. 6. Specific lymphosarcoma (x 100), conventionally called fungal mycosis; Fig. 7. Reticulosarcoma on histological examination at low magnification (x 200). Stained by silver; Fig. 8. Nodular lymphosarcoma mainly prolymphocytic, with small cells and indented nuclei: histology seen at high magnification (x 800); Fig. 9. Nodular lymphosarcoma, prolymphocytic and lymphoblastic (or lymphoblastoid), with large cells: histology seen at high magnification (x 800)*

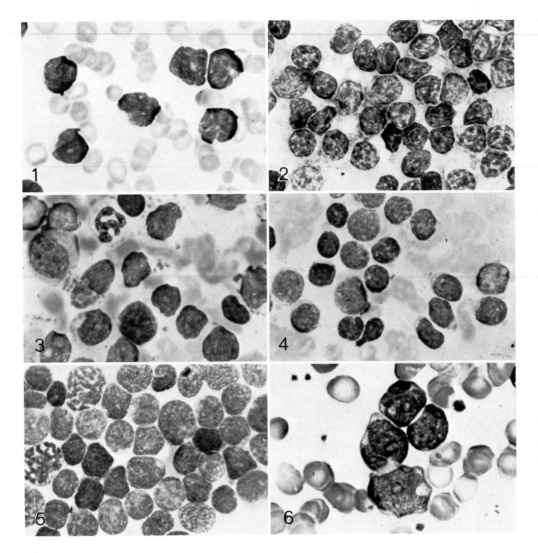

Plate I.
1. *Nodular lymphosarcoma, prolymphocytic (smear, Giemsa, x 1,000);*
2. *Diffuse lymphosarcoma, lymphocytic (smear, Giemsa, x 1,000);*
3. *Diffuse lymphosarcoma, lymphocytoplasmocytic (smear, Giemsa, x 1,000);*
4. *Diffuse lymphosarcoma, prolymphocytic (smear, Giemsa, x 1,000);*
5. *Diffuse lymphosarcoma, lymphoblastic (smear, Giemsa, x 1,000);*
6. *Diffuse thymic lymphosarcoma with convoluted nuclei (smear, Giemsa, x 1,000)*

2.2.1. The lymphocytic type, hardly recognizable histologically and
only identifiable cytologically on smears (Plate I.2) is exceptional
when detected in this way, since most of the cases recognized as such
are local lesions of chronic lymphoid leukemia (Fig. 10).

2.2.2. The lymphoplasmocytic type is easier to identify histologically,
but cytology is a valuable aid to lymphocyte recognition (Plate I.3).
As in the case of the lymphocytic type, a neoplasia diagnosed as lymphoplasmocytic lymphosarcoma is almost always a lesion of the systemic
disease called primary macroglobulinemia (Waldenström) (Fig. 11).

2.2.3. The prolymphocytic-lymphoblastic diffuse type (Plate I.4) is
considered to be developed from a nodular variety converted into a
diffuse architecture.

2.2.4. The lymphoblastic (or lymphoblastoid) type resembles a macrolymphoblastic acute lymphoid leukemia both histologically (Fig. 12)
and cytologically (Plate I.5), even though the cytoplasm in its cells
is often slightly more basophilic than the cytoplasm of the cells of
this type of leukemia.

One case of diffuse lymphoblastic lymphosarcoma is peculiar to the
convoluted shape of its cell nuclei; it is known as the convoluted nuclei lymphoblastic type (Plate I.6) (Fig. 13), and as a rule is characteristic of a clinical form of the disease which is of mediastinal
(? thymic) origin but very quickly develops into leukemia.

The immunoblastic type (13) is characterized by the peculiar appearance
of the cells: they are large (Figs. 14 and 15), and their cytoplasm
is hyperbasophilic and pyroninophilic, and contain numerous vacuoles
(Plate II.1 and 3) (14); in this they resemble acute lymphoid immunoblastic leukemia cells (Plate II.2) and, in histological section,
reticulin fibrils are rare (Fig. 16).

In Burkitt's true (African) lymphosarcoma (24) (Plate II.4, Fig. 17)[1]
the cells are very similar to those just described, but are smaller
and are therefore often considered as small immunoblasts; however,
both smears and sections are dotted with normal macrophages in a state
of phagocytosis ("starry sky" appearance).

In mycosis fungoides (Fig. 18), cell cytoplasm is abnormally extensive
for parts of the lymphoid strain (Plate II.5) (Fig. 19), which explains
the classic error in identifying this type of cell as a histiocyte.

Reticulosarcoma (RS) (Plate II.6, Figs. 20 and 21) is made up of mononuclear cells which include reticulin-producing cells, since silver
coloring shows up a dense network of fine reticulin fibers in this type
of tumor (Fig. 22). The classic reticular cells (17) therefore are
included in this category of cells. Some authors believe that RS is
made up of histiocytes (35) but, as has been seen, the definition of
this term varies from one author to another (Fig. 1).

---

[1] Burkitt's African lymphosarcomas are the only ones whose cell nuclei
almost always have an EBV genome, which is not the case in so-called
Burkitt's lymphosarcoma in other geographical areas. The latter
tumors are mostly lymphoblastic (or blastoid) lymphosarcomas, or
else ordinary immunoblastic lymphosarcomas with a few macrophages
in a stage of phagocytosis in their tissue. The great majority of
non-African so-called Burkitt's lymphosarcoma have no EBV genome in
their cell nuclei (7).

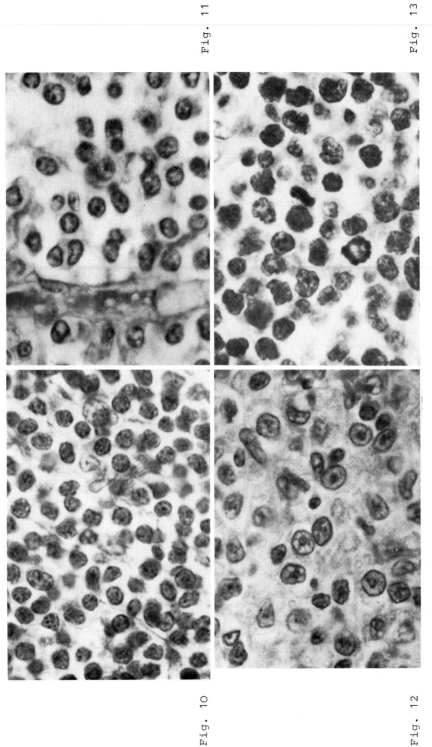

Fig. 10            Fig. 11

Fig. 12            Fig. 13

*Fig. 10. Lesions of a chronic lymphoid leukemia indistinguishable from a so-called diffuse lymphocytic lymphosarcoma: histology seen at high magnification (x 800); Fig. 11. Lesions of a primary macroglobulinemia (Waldenström) indistinguishable from a so-called diffuse lympho- plasmocytic lymphosarcoma: histology seen at high magnification (x 800); Fig. 12. Diffuse lymphoblastic lymphosarcoma: histology seen at high magnification (x 800); Fig. 13. Diffuse lymphoblastic lymphosarcoma with convoluted nuclei: histology seen at high magnification (x 800)*

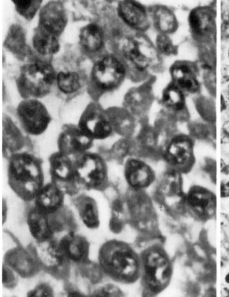

Fig. 14

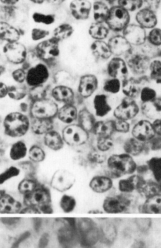

Fig. 15

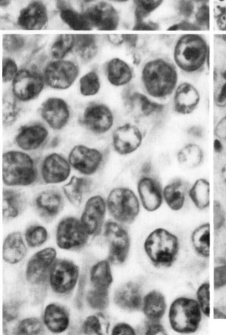

Fig. 16

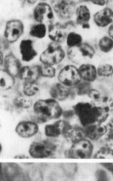

Fig. 17

Fig. 14. Diffuse immunoblastic T-lymphosarcoma: histology seen at high magnification (x 800); Fig. 15. Diffuse immunoblastic B-lymphosarcoma. Note the plasmacytoid tendency of certain immunoblasts (x 800);

Fig. 16. Scarcity of reticulin fibers in the immunoblastic lymphosarcoma (x 800); Fig. 17. Burkitt's lymphosarcoma: histology seen at high magnification (x 800)

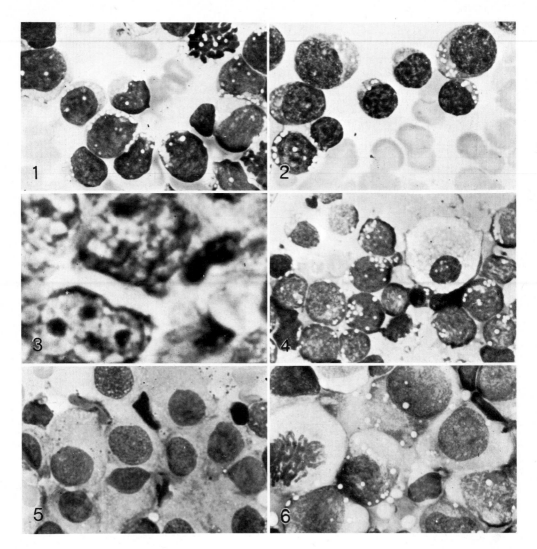

Plate II. 1. Immunoblastic lymphosarcoma T (smear, Giemsa, x 1,000);
2. Immunoblastic acute lymphoid leukaemia (smear, Giemsa, x 1,000);
3. Immunoblastic lymphosarcoma (section, methyl-green pyronin, x 1,5000);
4. Burkitt's African lymphosarcoma (smear, Giemsa, x 1,000);
5. Mycosis fungoides (smear, Giemsa, x 1,000);
6. Reticulosarcoma (smear, Giemsa, x 1,000)

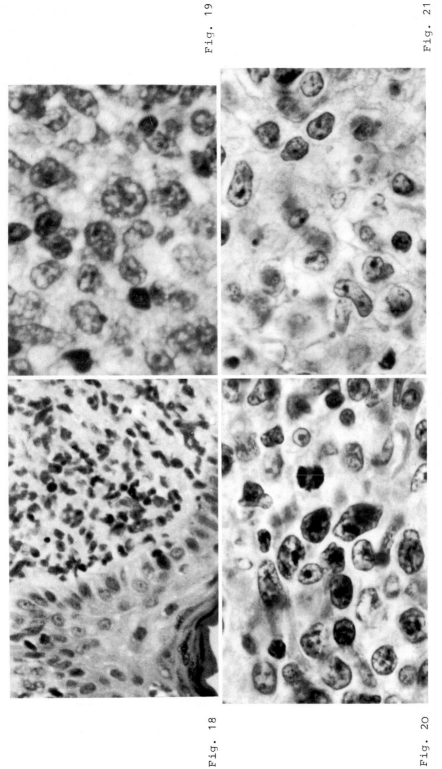

Fig. 19

Fig. 21

Fig. 18

Fig. 20

*Fig. 18. Mycosis fungoides: histology seen at medium magnification (x 200); Fig. 19. Mycosis fungoides: histology seen at high magnification (x 800); Fig. 20. Reticulosarcoma of lymphoid tissue: histology seen at high magnification (x 800); Fig. 21. Reticulosarcoma of bone tissue: histology seen at high magnification (x 800)*

Table 1. Lymphosarcomas and reticulosarcoma ("malignant lymphomas" or hematosarcomas) subclassification

| W.H.O. | | Equivalent Rappaport's classification terms[a] | Other terms[b] |
|---|---|---|---|
| **Nodular lymphosarcoma** | | | |
| Prolymphocytic or | | | |
| Prolymphocytic and lymphoblastic | | | |
| Cleaved cells[c] | Small cells | Lymphocytic, well or poorly differentiated | Centrocytic (Lennert); follicle cells, small (Bennett et al.) |
| | Mixed cells | Mixed (lymphocytic-histiocytic) | Centroblastic-centrocytic (Lennert); follicle cells, mixed (Bennett et al.) |
| Noncleaved cells[c] | Large cells | Histiocytic | Centroblastic-centrocytic (Lennert); follicle cells, large (Bennett et al.) |
| **Diffuse lymphosarcoma** | | | |
| Lymphocytic | | Lymphocytic, well differentiated | |
| Lymphocytoplasmocytic | | | Immunocytoma (Lennert) |
| Prolymphocytic or | | | |
| Prolymphocytic and lymphoblastic | | | |
| Cleaved cells[c] | Small cells | Lymphocytic, poor differentiated | Centrocytic (Lennert); follicle cells, small (Bennett et al.) |
| | Mixed cells | Mixed (lymphocytic-histiocytic) | Centroblastic-centrocytic (Lennert); follicle cells, mixed (Bennett et al.) |
| Noncleaved cells[c] | Large cells[d] | Histiocytic | Centroblastic-centrocytic (Lennert); follicle cells, large (Bennett et al.) |
| Lymphoblastic including a convoluted type | | Lymphocytic, poorly differentiated | |
| Immunoblastic[d,e] | | Histiocytic | Large lymphoid pyroninophilic (Dorfman); undifferentiated large cells (Bennett et al.) |
| Burkitt's tumor | | | Small noncleaved follicular center cell tumors (Lukes and Collins) |

Table 1. (continued)

| W.H.O. | Equivalent Rappaport's classification terms[a] | Other terms |
|---|---|---|
| Diffuse lymphosarcoma | | |
|   Mycosis fungoides | | |
| Reticulosarcoma[d,e] | Histiocytic | Histiocytic (Lukes and Collins; Dorfman), "True histiocytic" (Bennett et al.) |

a See ref. 25.

b See ref. 35.

c Subdivision according to Lukes and Collins (9).

d Diagnostic problem of large cells diffuse hematosarcomas (or "lymphomas").

e The entity of "immunoblastic" lymphosarcomas was recognized in Lukes' and Collins', Lennert's and Mathé's classifications presented at this workshop.

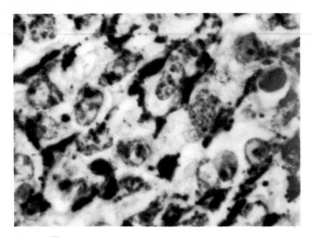

*Fig. 22. Reticulin in a reticulosarcoma. Note the fine pericellular net-work of reticulin fibers (x 800)*

Table 1 lists the different categories of non-Hodgkin's hematosarcoma, and mentions the classification which was chosen for the W.H.O. Leukemia and Hematosarcoma Reference Center.

3. Today, the study of immunological markers (2, 27) in neoplastic cells has made it possible to identify mycosis fungoides cells as T-lymphocytes, whereas in Burkitt's (African) lymphosarcoma and nodular lymphosarcoma the cells are B-lymphocytes and in diffused lymphosarcomas, they can be either B- or T-lymphocytes (6, 8, 9, 12, 13, 26). In the latter case, cells of the lymphocytic, lymphocyto-plasmocytic, pro-lymphocyto-lymphoblastic, and Burkitt's types may be considered as B cells, the mycosis fungoides and convoluted nucleus lymphoblastic types as T cells, and the remaining lymphoblastic types are either B or T cells.

Finally, morphological aspects of these different hematosarcomas as shown by transmission electron microscopy and scanning electron microscopy are being studied by DANTCHEV (5) and the preliminary results will be included in another volume of this series.

REFERENCES

1. Aschoff, L.: Das Reticulo-endothelial System. Ergebn. Inn. Med. Linderheilh. 26, 1 (1924)
2. Belpomme, D., Dantchev, D., Karima, M., Lelarge, N., Joseph, R., Caillou, B., Lafleur, M., Mathé, G.: Search for correlation between immunological and morphological criteria used to classifiy lymphoid leukemias and non-Hodgkin's hematosarcomas with special reference to scanning electron microscopy and T and B membrane markers. This volume, pp. 131 - 143.
3. Brill, N.E., Baehr, G., Rosenthal, N.: Generalized giant lymph folli-cle hyperplasia of lymph nodes and spleen. J. Am. Med. Assoc. 84, 688 (1925)
4. Burkitt, D.P., Wright, D.H.: Burkitt's lymphoma. Edinburgh: Living-stone, 1970

5. Dantchev, D.: Revised semiology of the different mononuclear cells under scanning electron microscopy. This volume, pp. 8-15
6. Davies, A.J.S.: Personal communication
7. Hausen, H. zur: Oncogenic herpes viruses. Biophys. Acta 417, 25 (1975)
8. Lennert, K., Stein, H., Kaiserling, E.: Cytological and functional criteria for the classification of malignant lymphomata. Brit. J. Cancer 31, 29 (1975)
9. Lukes, R.J., Collins, R.D.: New approaches to the classification of the lymphomata. Brit. J. Cancer 31, 1, Suppl. II (1975)
10. Mathé, G.: Active Immunotherapy of Cancer, its immunoprophylaxis and immunorestoration. Heidelberg and New York: Springer-Verlag, in press, 1976, Vol. 1
11. Mathé, G.: L'inventaire préthérapeutique moderne de la néoplasie clef du prognostic et de l'espérance de guérison dans les hémato-sarcomes (lymphomes). La maladie de Hodgkin. Concours Méd. 97, 4777 (1975)
12. Mathé, G., Belpomme, D.: T and B Lymphocytic nature of leukemias and lymphosarcomas: a new but still uncertain parameter for their classification. Biomed. 20, 81 (1974)
13. Mathé, G., Belpomme, D., Dantchev, D., Pouillart, P.: Progress in the classification of lymphoid and/or monocytoid leukemias and of lympho-reticulosarcomas. Biomed. 22, 177 (1975)
14. Mathé, G., Belpomme, D., Dantchev, D., Khalil, A., Afifi, A.M., Taleb, M., Pouillart, P., Schwarzenberg, L., Hayat, M., De Vassal, F., Jasmin, C., Misset, J.L., Musset, M.: Immunoblastic lymphosar-coma: a cytological and clinical entity? Biomed. 22, 473 (1975)
15. Mathé, G., Belpomme, D., Dantchev, D., Pouillart, P., Jasmin, C., Misset, J.L., Musset, M., Amiel, J.L., Schlumberger, J.R., Schwar-zenberg, L., Hayat, M., De Vassal, F., Lafleur, M.: Immunoblastic acute lymphoid leukaemia. Biomed. 20, 333 (1974)
16. Mathé, G., Belpomme, D., Pouillart, P., Schwarzenberg, L., Misset, J.L., Jasmin, C., Musset, M., Cattan, A., Amiel, J.L., Schneider, M.: Preliminary results of an immunotherapy trial of terminal leukemic lymphosarcoma. Biomed. 23, 465 (1975)
17. Mathé, G., Dantchev, D., Pouillart, P., Florentin, I.: De l'hémato-logie avec à 1 hématologie sans microscope. Nouv. Presse Méd. 1 3135 (1972)
18. Mathé, G., Kenis, Y.: La chimiothérapie des cancers (leucémies, hématosarcomes et tumeurs solides). Paris: Expansion Scientifique, 1975, 3rd ed.
19. Mathé, G., Rappaport, H.: Histocytological typing of the neoplastic diseases of the haematopoietic and lymphoid tissues. Geneva: W.H.O., 1976
20. Mathé, G., Seman, G.: Aspects histologiques et cytologiques des leucémies et hématosarcomes. Paris: Maloine, 1963
21. Mathé, G., Tubiana, M. (eds.): Natural history diagnosis and treat-ment of Hodgkin's disease. Copenhagen: Munksgaard, 1973, Vol. 2
22. Misset, J.L., Pouillart, P., Amiel, J.L., Schwarzenberg, L., Hayat, M., De Vassal, F., Musset, M., Belpomme, D., Jasmin, C., Albahary, C., Depierre, R., Mathé, G.: Combinaison d'adriamycine, de VM 2, de cyclophosphamide et de prednisone (AVmCP) pour la chimiothérapie des lymphosarcomes et réticulosarcomes aux stades ou formes topo-graphiques III et IV. Nouv. Presse Méd. 4, 3117 (1975)
23. Oberling, G.: Les réticulosarcomes et les réticulo-endothéliosar-comes de la moelle osseuse (saecomes d'Ewing). Bull. Ass. Fr. Cancer 17, 259 (1928)
24. O'Conor, G.T.: In: Histopathological classification of Burkitt's tumour. Bull. World Org. 40, 601 (1969)
25. Rappaport, H.: Tumors of the hemopoietic systems. In: Atlas of Human Pathology. Washington D.C., Armed Forces Inst. Pathol., 1966

26. Seligmann, M., Preud'homme, J.L., Brouet, J.C.: B and T cell markers in human proliferative blood diseases and primary immunodeficiencies with special reference to membrane bound immunoglobulins. Transplant. Rev. 16, 85 (1973)
27. Seligmann, M., Preud'homme, J.L., Brouet, J.C.: Surface cell markers in human lymphoid malignancies. This volume, pp.
28. Symmers, D.: Follicular lymphadenomegaly with splenomegaly. A newly recognized disease of lymphatic system. Arch. Path. 3, 816 (1927)
29. Turk, J.L.: Immunology in Clinical Medicine. London: Heinemann, 1969
30. Van Furth, R., Cohn, Z.A.: The origin and kinetics of mononuclear phagocytes. J. Exp. Med. 128, 415 (1968)
31. Van Furth, R., Cohn, Z.A., Hirsch, J.G., Humprey, J.H., Spector, W.G., Langevoort, H.L.: The mononuclear phagocyte system: a new classification of macrophages, monocytes and their precusor cells. Bull. O.M.S. 46, 845 (1972)
32. Van Furth, R., Diesselhoff-Den Dulk, M.M.C.: The kinetics of promonocytes and monocytes in the bone marrow. J. Exp. Med. 132, 813. (1970)
33. Virchow, R.: Die Krankhaften Geschwülste. Berlin: Hirschweld, 1863, Vol. 1
34. Volkman, A., Gowans, J.L.: The origin of macrophages from bone marrow in the rat. Brit. J. Exp. Path. 46, 60 (1965)
35. Workshop for Classification of non-Hodgkin's Lymphomas. Warrenton, Virginia, 4-5, Sept. 1975. Report in Biomed. 22, 466 (1975).
36. Wilson, F.: Personal communication

# Recent Results in Cancer Research

Sponsored by the Swiss League against Cancer. Editor in Chief: P. Rentchnick, Genève